AQA Anthology of Poetry

Power and Conflict

OK, we'll admit it — the poems in AQA's *Power and Conflict* cluster aren't exactly a barrel of laughs. But on the bright side, this CGP Workbook will give you plenty of reasons to be optimistic about the exam...

It's packed with brilliant questions to test you on everything you'll need to know, from language, structure and form to themes, techniques and context.

Better still, it's all topped off with plenty of exam practice, so you'll be more than ready to deal with anything the examiners can fire at you on the day!

The Workbook

CONTENTS

Section One — The Poems

Section Two — Themes

CONTENTS

Section Three — Poetic Techniques

Section Four — Exam Buster

Published by CGP

Editors:
James Summersgill
Matt Topping
Sean Walsh

With thanks to Emma Crighton and Nicola Woodfin for the proofreading.
With thanks to Jan Greenway for the copyright research.

Acknowledgements:

Cover quote from 'The Charge of the Light Brigade' by Alfred Tennyson.

'Exposure' by Wilfred Owen from *Wilfred Owen: The War Poems*, edited by Jon Stallworthy (Chatto and Windus, 1994).

'Storm on the Island' by Seamus Heaney from *Opened Ground*. Faber and Faber Ltd.

'Bayonet Charge' by Ted Hughes from *Collected Poems*. Faber and Faber Ltd.

'Remains' by Simon Armitage from *The Not Dead* (2008) reprinted by permission of Pomona.

'Poppies' by Jane Weir: Copyright Templar Poetry from *The Way I Dressed During the Revolution* (Templar, 2010).

'War Photographer' from *Standing Female Nude* by Carol Ann Duffy. Published by Anvil Press Poetry, 1985. Copyright © Carol Ann Duffy. Reproduced by permission of the author c/o Rogers, Coleridge & White., 20 Powis Mews, London, W11 1JN.

'Tissue' by Imtiaz Dharker from *The Terrorist at my Table* published by Bloodaxe Books, 2006. Reproduced by Bloodaxe Books on behalf of the author.

'The Emigrée' by Carol Rumens. Reprinted by kind permission of Carol Rumens.

'Kamikaze' by Beatrice Garland: Copyright Templar Poetry from *The Invention of Fireworks* (Templar, 2013).

'Checking Out Me History' copyright © 1996 by John Agard, reproduced by kind permission of John Agard c/o Caroline Sheldon Literary Agency Ltd.

Every effort has been made to locate copyright holders and obtain permission to reproduce sources. For those sources where it has been difficult to trace the copyright holder of the work, we would be grateful for information. If any copyright holder would like us to make an amendment to the acknowledgements, please notify us and we will gladly update the book at the next reprint. Thank you.

ISBN: 978 1 78294 819 3

Printed by Elanders Ltd, Newcastle upon Tyne.

Clipart from Corel®

Based on the classic CGP style created by Richard Parsons.

Text, design, layout and original illustrations © Coordination Group Publications Ltd. (CGP) 2017

How to Use this Book

Practise the three main skills you'll need for the exam

Each question tests <u>one or more</u> of the <u>three skills</u> you'll be tested on in the <u>exam</u>. You'll need to:

1) Write about the poems in a <u>thoughtful way</u>, making <u>clear comparisons</u> and <u>picking out</u> appropriate <u>examples</u> and <u>quotations</u> to back up your points and opinions.

2) <u>Identify</u> and <u>explain</u> features of <u>form</u>, <u>structure</u> and <u>language</u>. Using <u>subject terminology</u>, show how the poets use these <u>effectively</u> to create meanings and effects.

3) Refer to the <u>context</u> of the poems, making clear links between the <u>context</u> and the <u>text</u>.

Renée was disappointed that she wouldn't be assessed on her ability to illustrate the poems.

Use this workbook with or without the CGP Poetry Guide

1) This workbook is perfect to use with CGP's 'Power and Conflict' <u>Poetry Guide</u>. The workbook covers <u>each poem</u> and <u>every section</u> of the Poetry Guide, so you can test your knowledge <u>step by step</u>.

2) You can also use this book <u>by itself</u>. It covers all the <u>important</u> parts of the poems, including <u>language</u>, <u>structure</u>, <u>form</u>, <u>themes</u>, <u>context</u> and <u>poetic techniques</u>.

3) This book includes a <u>copy of every poem</u>, so you won't need to go rooting around for your anthology. You can also <u>annotate</u> the poems with your own <u>notes</u> and <u>comments</u>.

It prepares you for the exam every step of the way

1) There are <u>hundreds of questions</u> throughout the book that test your knowledge of <u>all fifteen poems</u>.

2) Section 1 contains <u>revision tasks</u> designed to help you compare poems and develop personal responses — these tasks <u>aren't</u> exam style. Throughout the rest of the book there are plenty of <u>practice exam questions</u> so you can use what you've revised to write <u>realistic answers</u>.

3) Section 4 is jam-packed with useful <u>exam advice</u>. It <u>guides</u> you through how to tackle the exam, and there's a <u>mark scheme</u> that you can use to mark <u>sample answers</u> and improve answers of your <u>own</u>.

4) Each section contains at least one '<u>Skills Focus</u>' page. These pages help you to practise important skills <u>individually</u>. You can tackle them in <u>any order</u> and prioritise the skills you find the <u>hardest</u>.

5) You can find <u>answers</u> to all of the <u>questions</u> and <u>tasks</u> at the back of the book. These are <u>examples</u> of what you could have written, but there can be lots of valid answers when it comes to writing about poetry — just make sure your points are <u>well-explained</u> and supported by <u>evidence</u>.

How not to use this book: underwater, upside down, in the dark...

You don't have to work through this book in order. If you wanted to, you could ease yourself in with the poems you're more familiar with, or you could prioritise your weaknesses and face them head on — the choice is yours.

Section One — The Poems

Ozymandias

I met a traveller from an antique land
Who said: 'Two vast and trunkless legs of stone
Stand in the desert. Near them, on the sand,
Half sunk, a shatter'd visage lies, whose frown,
5 And wrinkled lip, and sneer of cold command,
Tell that its sculptor well those passions read
Which yet survive, stamp'd on these lifeless things,
The hand that mock'd them and the heart that fed;
And on the pedestal these words appear:
10 "My name is Ozymandias, king of kings:
Look on my works, ye Mighty, and despair!"
Nothing beside remains. Round the decay
Of that colossal wreck, boundless and bare
The lone and level sands stretch far away.'

Percy Bysshe Shelley

Q1 What does the phrase "**Half sunk, a shatter'd visage lies**" (line 4) tell you about the statue?

....

....

Q2 What is the effect of the word "**mock'd**" in line 8 of the poem?

....

....

....

Q3 Find a quote that addresses each of the following themes and explain the effect of the quote.

Theme	Quote	Explanation
Arrogance		
Loss of power		

Q4 Explain the importance of irony in the poem. Use an example to support your answer.

....

....

....

....

Q5 What does the poem suggest about the power of art?

....

....

....

....

The power of art was a particularly thought-provoking topic for Frank.

Q6 'Romantic' poets such as Shelley strongly believed in the power of nature. Choose one quote that shows how 'Romanticism' might have influenced the poem. Explain your choice.

Quote: ....

....

Explanation: ....

....

....

Q7 What impression do you think the poet is trying to achieve by describing the statue from the traveller's point of view?

....

....

....

....

Antiqueland — the world's oldest theme park...

COMPARE POEMS

Read 'My Last Duchess' by Robert Browning, on page 8, and then compare it with 'Ozymandias'.
* How is art presented in each poem?
* What do the poems suggest about how human power and art are linked?

London

> I wander through each chartered street,
> Near where the chartered Thames does flow,
> And mark in every face I meet
> Marks of weakness, marks of woe.
>
> 5   In every cry of every man,
> In every infant's cry of fear,
> In every voice, in every ban,
> The mind-forged manacles I hear.
>
> How the chimney-sweeper's cry
> 10   Every black'ning church appals,
> And the hapless soldier's sigh
> Runs in blood down palace walls.
>
> But most through midnight streets I hear
> How the youthful harlot's curse
> 15   Blasts the new-born infant's tear,
> And blights with plagues the marriage hearse.
>
> *William Blake*

Q1 What does the first stanza tell you the speaker is doing?

....

....

Q2 What is the rhyme scheme in the poem? Explain the effect it has.

....

....

....

Q3 Using an example, explain how Blake's use of emotive language affects the message of the poem.

....

....

....

....

Q4 Find a quote that addresses each of the following themes and explain the effect of the quote.

Theme	Quote	Explanation
Hopelessness		
Individual experience of place		

Q5 What does the phrase "**the hapless soldier's sigh / Runs in blood down palace walls**" (lines 11-12) suggest about the narrator's opinion of people in power?

....

....

....

Q6 What is the effect of each of these techniques in the poem?

Repetition: ....

....

Contrast: ....

....

Q7 Why do you think the poet chose the form of a monologue for the poem?

....

....

....

....

> *It's certainly not your typical stroll along the Thames...*
>
> 'The Emigrée', by Carol Rumens (page 26), also features a narrator who thinks about place.
> - Which poem do you find more emotive in its presentation of place?
> - In these poems, how does the narrator's distance from a place affect their presentation of it?

The Prelude: Stealing the Boat

One summer evening (led by her) I found
A little boat tied to a willow tree
Within a rocky cave, its usual home.
Straight I unloosed her chain, and stepping in
5 Pushed from the shore. It was an act of stealth
And troubled pleasure, nor without the voice
Of mountain-echoes did my boat move on;
Leaving behind her still, on either side,
Small circles glittering idly in the moon,
10 Until they melted all into one track
Of sparkling light. But now, like one who rows,
Proud of his skill, to reach a chosen point
With an unswerving line, I fixed my view
Upon the summit of a craggy ridge,
15 The horizon's utmost boundary; far above
Was nothing but the stars and the grey sky.
She was an elfin pinnace; lustily
I dipped my oars into the silent lake,
And, as I rose upon the stroke, my boat
20 Went heaving through the water like a swan;
When, from behind that craggy steep till then
The horizon's bound, a huge peak, black and huge,

As if with voluntary power instinct,
Upreared its head. I struck and struck again,
25 And growing still in stature the grim shape
Towered up between me and the stars, and still,
For so it seemed, with purpose of its own
And measured motion like a living thing,
Strode after me. With trembling oars I turned,
30 And through the silent water stole my way
Back to the covert of the willow tree;
There in her mooring-place I left my bark, –
And through the meadows homeward went, in grave
And serious mood; but after I had seen
35 That spectacle, for many days, my brain
Worked with a dim and undetermined sense
Of unknown modes of being; o'er my thoughts
There hung a darkness, call it solitude
Or blank desertion. No familiar shapes
40 Remained, no pleasant images of trees,
Of sea or sky, no colours of green fields;
But huge and mighty forms, that do not live
Like living men, moved slowly through the mind
By day, and were a trouble to my dreams.

William Wordsworth

Q1   Find a quote to illustrate each of the following statements.

    a) The narrator feels confident handling the boat.

    ....

    b) The narrator feels intimidated by the mountain.

    ....

Q2   Describe the tone at the beginning of the extract. How does Wordsworth create this tone?

    ....

    ....

    ....

Q3   Which line of the extract acts as a turning point? Explain how the extract changes from this point.

    Line: ....

    Explanation: ....

    ....

    ....

Q4 Find a quote to illustrate each of the following techniques.
In each case, briefly explain the effect of technique.

Technique	Quote	Explanation
Personification		
Oxymoron		
Simile		

Q5 Explain the effect of the following features of the extract's form.

Lack of rhyme: ....

....

Rhythm: ....

....

Q6 The 'Romantics' often wrote about the connection between nature and human emotion. Give one quote to show how 'Romanticism' might have influenced this extract. Explain your choice.

Quote: ....

Explanation: ....

....

....

....

That's just part of an introduction to a prelude? Blimey...

Read 'Ozymandias' by Percy Bysshe Shelley, on page 2, and compare it with 'The Prelude'.
- In what ways do Shelley and Wordsworth present human arrogance?
- How do they compare this human arrogance with the power of nature?

My Last Duchess

Ferrara

That's my last Duchess painted on the wall,
Looking as if she were alive. I call
That piece a wonder, now: Frà Pandolf's hands
Worked busily a day, and there she stands.
5 Will't please you sit and look at her? I said
'Frà Pandolf' by design, for never read
Strangers like you that pictured countenance,
The depth and passion of its earnest glance,
But to myself they turned (since none puts by
10 The curtain I have drawn for you, but I)
And seemed as they would ask me, if they durst
How such a glance came there; so, not the first
Are you to turn and ask thus. Sir, 'twas not
Her husband's presence only, called that spot
15 Of joy into the Duchess' cheek: perhaps
Frà Pandolf chanced to say 'Her mantle laps
Over my lady's wrist too much,' or 'Paint
Must never hope to reproduce the faint
Half-flush that dies along her throat': such stuff
20 Was courtesy, she thought, and cause enough
For calling up that spot of joy. She had
A heart – how shall I say? – too soon made glad,
Too easily impressed; she liked whate'er
She looked on, and her looks went everywhere.
25 Sir, 'twas all one! My favour at her breast,
The dropping of the daylight in the West,
The bough of cherries some officious fool
Broke in the orchard for her, the white mule

She rode with round the terrace – all and each
30 Would draw from her alike the approving speech,
Or blush, at least. She thanked men, – good! but thanked
Somehow – I know not how – as if she ranked
My gift of a nine-hundred-years-old name
With anybody's gift. Who'd stoop to blame
35 This sort of trifling? Even had you skill
In speech – (which I have not) – to make your will
Quite clear to such an one, and say, 'Just this
Or that in you disgusts me; here you miss,
Or there exceed the mark' – and if she let
40 Herself be lessoned so, nor plainly set
Her wits to yours, forsooth, and made excuse,
– E'en then would be some stooping; and I choose
Never to stoop. Oh sir, she smiled, no doubt,
Whene'er I passed her; but who passed without
45 Much the same smile? This grew; I gave commands;
Then all smiles stopped together. There she stands
As if alive. Will't please you rise? We'll meet
The company below, then. I repeat,
The Count your master's known munificence
50 Is ample warrant that no just pretence
Of mine for dowry will be disallowed;
Though his fair daughter's self, as I avowed
At starting, is my object. Nay, we'll go
Together down, sir. Notice Neptune, though,
55 Taming a sea-horse, thought a rarity,
Which Claus of Innsbruck cast in bronze for me!

Robert Browning

Q1 Browning often hints at things rather than telling you directly about
them. What can you work out from each of the following quotes?

a) **"since none puts by / The curtain I have drawn for you, but I"** (lines 9-10)

....

b) **"And seemed as they would ask me, if they durst"** (line 11)

....

c) **"I gave commands; / Then all smiles stopped together."** (lines 45-46)

....

Q2 What is the rhyme scheme in the poem? Explain the effect it has.

....

....

Q3   Why do you think the Duke has a portrait of his last Duchess on display?

....

....

....

Q4   Find a quote that addresses each of the following themes and explain the effect of the quote.

Theme	Quote	Explanation
Jealousy		
Pride		

Q5   Explain the effect of the following features in the poem.

Enjambment: ....

....

Rhetorical questions: ....

....

Q6   Do you think the Duke is a reliable narrator? Give evidence to support your answer.

....

....

....

....

....

Will't please you sit and look at this task...

What is the significance of the Duke's visitor in the poem? Write about:

• What their presence reveals about the events surrounding the poem.
• The impact of their lack of voice on the tone of the poem.

Jess had never
been fond
of sitting for
portraits.

The Charge of the Light Brigade

I

Half a league, half a league,
Half a league onward,
All in the valley of Death
    Rode the six hundred.
5 'Forward, the Light Brigade!
Charge for the guns!' he said:
Into the valley of Death
    Rode the six hundred.

II

'Forward, the Light Brigade!'
10 Was there a man dismay'd?
Not tho' the soldier knew
    Some one had blunder'd:
Theirs not to make reply,
Theirs not to reason why,
15 Theirs but to do and die:
Into the valley of Death
    Rode the six hundred.

III

Cannon to right of them,
Cannon to left of them,
20 Cannon in front of them
    Volley'd and thunder'd;
Storm'd at with shot and shell,
Boldly they rode and well,
Into the jaws of Death,
25 Into the mouth of Hell
    Rode the six hundred.

IV

Flash'd all their sabres bare,
Flash'd as they turn'd in air
Sabring the gunners there,
30 Charging an army, while
    All the world wonder'd:
Plunged in the battery-smoke
Right thro' the line they broke;
Cossack and Russian
35 Reel'd from the sabre stroke
    Shatter'd and sunder'd.
Then they rode back, but not
    Not the six hundred.

V

Cannon to right of them,
40 Cannon to left of them,
Cannon behind them
    Volley'd and thunder'd;
Storm'd at with shot and shell,
While horse and hero fell,
45 They that had fought so well
Came thro' the jaws of Death
Back from the mouth of Hell,
All that was left of them,
    Left of six hundred.

VI

50 When can their glory fade?
O the wild charge they made!
    All the world wonder'd.
Honour the charge they made!
Honour the Light Brigade,
55   Noble six hundred!

Alfred Tennyson

Q1   Read lines 1-4 and explain what is happening here.

....

....

....

Q2   What is the effect of the narrator referring to the soldiers as "**the six hundred**" (line 4)?

....

....

Q3 Find a quote to illustrate each of the following techniques.
Explain the effect of the technique in each quote.

Technique	Quote	Explanation
Repetition		
Onomatopoeia		

Q4 Why do you think the poet chose to use a third-person narrator? What effect does this create?

....

....

....

Q5 Explain the effect of each of the following quotes.

a) **"Storm'd at with shot and shell"** (line 22)

....

....

b) **"Into the jaws of Death, / Into the mouth of Hell"** (lines 24-25)

....

....

Q6 To what extent do you think the poem romanticises the Charge
of the Light Brigade? Give evidence to support your answer.

....

....

....

....

PERSONAL RESPONSE

Poems to the left of you, poems to the right of you...

'Remains', by Simon Armitage (page 18), is another poem that features violent language and imagery.
- In each poem, how does this language and imagery make you feel?
- How do the other techniques in the poems affect the presentation of violence?

Exposure

Our brains ache, in the merciless iced east winds that knive us...
Wearied we keep awake because the night is silent...
Low, drooping flares confuse our memory of the salient...
Worried by silence, sentries whisper, curious, nervous,
5   But nothing happens.

Watching, we hear the mad gusts tugging on the wire,
Like twitching agonies of men among its brambles.
Northward, incessantly, the flickering gunnery rumbles,
Far off, like a dull rumour of some other war.
10   What are we doing here?

The poignant misery of dawn begins to grow...
We only know war lasts, rain soaks, and clouds sag stormy.
Dawn massing in the east her melancholy army
Attacks once more in ranks on shivering ranks of grey,
15   But nothing happens.

Sudden successive flights of bullets streak the silence.
Less deathly than the air that shudders black with snow,
With sidelong flowing flakes that flock, pause, and renew;
We watch them wandering up and down the wind's nonchalance,
20   But nothing happens.

Pale flakes with fingering stealth come feeling for our faces –
We cringe in holes, back on forgotten dreams, and stare, snow-dazed,
Deep into grassier ditches. So we drowse, sun-dozed,
Littered with blossoms trickling where the blackbird fusses,
25   – Is it that we are dying?

Slowly our ghosts drag home: glimpsing the sunk fires, glozed
With crusted dark-red jewels; crickets jingle there;
For hours the innocent mice rejoice: the house is theirs;
Shutters and doors, all closed: on us the doors are closed, –
30   We turn back to our dying.

Since we believe not otherwise can kind fires burn;
Nor ever suns smile true on child, or field, or fruit.
For God's invincible spring our love is made afraid;
Therefore, not loath, we lie out here; therefore were born,
35   For love of God seems dying.

Tonight, this frost will fasten on this mud and us,
Shrivelling many hands, puckering foreheads crisp.
The burying-party, picks and shovels in shaking grasp,
Pause over half-known faces. All their eyes are ice,
40   But nothing happens.

Wilfred Owen

Q1   Describe how nature is presented in the poem.

....

....

....

Q2 How does the form of the poem affect the tone?

....

....

....

Q3 For each of the following quotes, identify one technique that is used and explain its effect.

    a) "**Pale flakes with fingering stealth come feeling for our faces –**" (line 21)

Technique: ....

Effect: ....

....

    b) "**All their eyes are ice**" (line 39)

Technique: ....

Effect: ....

....

Q4 What is the effect of using the first-person plural ("**we**", "**our**" and "**us**") in the poem?

....

....

....

Q5 To what extent do you think the soldiers believe that their sacrifice is worthwhile? Give evidence to support your answer.

....

....

....

....

COMPARE POEMS

If nothing is happening right now, try these questions...

Read 'London' by William Blake, on page 4, which is a similarly bleak poem.
- How do the poets use imagery to convey a feeling of hopelessness?
- Which poem do you find more emotive? Consider the context of each poem in your answer.

Storm on the Island

We are prepared: we build our houses squat,
Sink walls in rock and roof them with good slate.
This wizened earth has never troubled us
With hay, so, as you can see, there are no stacks
5 Or stooks that can be lost. Nor are there trees
Which might prove company when it blows full
Blast: you know what I mean – leaves and branches
Can raise a tragic chorus in a gale
So that you can listen to the thing you fear
10 Forgetting that it pummels your house too.
But there are no trees, no natural shelter.
You might think that the sea is company,
Exploding comfortably down on the cliffs
But no: when it begins, the flung spray hits
15 The very windows, spits like a tame cat
Turned savage. We just sit tight while wind dives
And strafes invisibly. Space is a salvo.
We are bombarded by the empty air.
Strange, it is a huge nothing that we fear.

Seamus Heaney

Q1 Find a quote to support each of the following statements.

  a) The islanders can't do anything while the storm rages outside.

  ....

  b) The island is a relatively lonely place.

  ....

Q2 In what way does the island setting contribute to the feeling of the poem?

  ....

  ....

Q3 Why do you think Heaney uses so many negatives (e.g. **"never"**, **"no"**, **"nothing"**) in the poem?

  ....

  ....

Q4 Find a quote that addresses each of the following themes and explain the effect of the quote.

Theme	Quote	Explanation
Security		
Fear		

Q5 Explain the effects of the following features in the poem.

Direct address: ....

....

Sibilance: ....

....

Q6 What does the simile "**the flung spray [...] spits like a tame cat / Turned savage**" (lines 14-16) suggest about nature?

....

....

....

Forget slate — some people try to beat nature at its own game.

Q7 To what extent do you think the phrase "**Exploding comfortably**" (line 13) reflects the overall tone of the poem? Give evidence to support your answer.

....

....

....

....

....

PERSONAL RESPONSE

My singing — a tragic chorus? How very dare you...

Heaney manages to pack a lot into a relatively short poem. Briefly answer the following questions:
- How would the poem be different if the personal pronoun 'I' had been used instead of 'we'?
- Do you think the poem presents the islanders as helpless? Explain your answer.

Bayonet Charge

Suddenly he awoke and was running – raw
In raw-seamed hot khaki, his sweat heavy,
Stumbling across a field of clods towards a green hedge
That dazzled with rifle fire, hearing
5   Bullets smacking the belly out of the air –
He lugged a rifle numb as a smashed arm;
The patriotic tear that had brimmed in his eye
Sweating like molten iron from the centre of his chest, –

In bewilderment then he almost stopped –
10   In what cold clockwork of the stars and the nations
Was he the hand pointing that second? He was running
Like a man who has jumped up in the dark and runs
Listening between his footfalls for the reason
Of his still running, and his foot hung like
15   Statuary in mid-stride. Then the shot-slashed furrows

Threw up a yellow hare that rolled like a flame
And crawled in a threshing circle, its mouth wide
Open silent, its eyes standing out.
He plunged past with his bayonet toward the green hedge,
20   King, honour, human dignity, etcetera
Dropped like luxuries in a yelling alarm
To get out of that blue crackling air
His terror's touchy dynamite.

Ted Hughes

Q1   How does the first line set the tone for the rest of the poem?

....

....

Q2   Find a quote that addresses each of the following themes and explain the effect of the quote.

Theme	Quote	Explanation
Fear		
Confusion		

Q3 Find an example of onomatopoeia in the poem and explain its effect.

Example: ....

Effect: ....

....

Q4 How does the soldier's state of mind shift throughout the poem?

....

....

....

Q5 What is suggested about the soldier in the phrase "**In what cold clockwork of the stars and the nations / Was he the hand pointing that second?**" (lines 10-11)?

....

....

....

Q6 Why do you think the poet shifts the focus in line 15 at the end of the second stanza rather than at the start of the third?

....

....

....

"Did someone say charge?"

Q7 What does the poem suggest about patriotism? Give evidence to support your answer.

....

....

....

....

On a happier note, you're now over halfway through the poems...

How does Hughes use language to present the reality of war? Write a couple of paragraphs about:

- Whether his use of figurative language helps the reader to sympathise with the soldier.
- How effective his use of violent language is in conveying the reality of war.

Remains

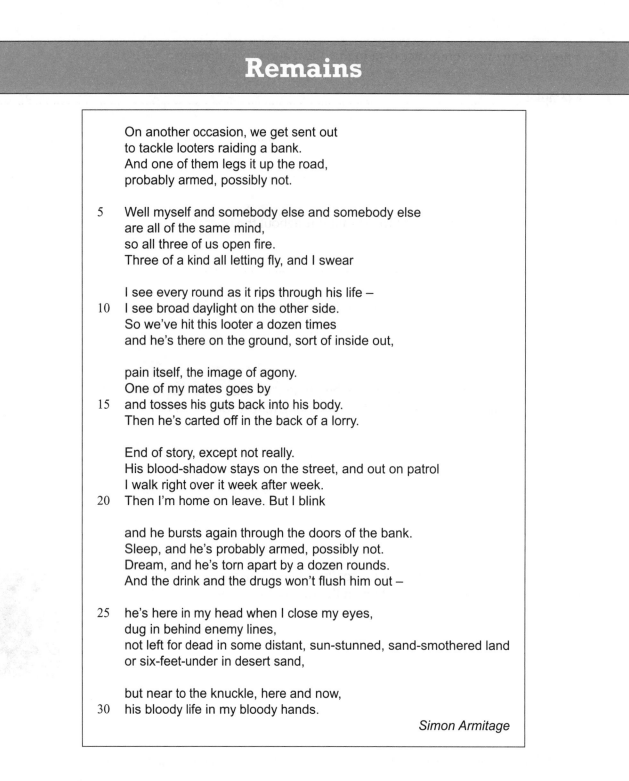

On another occasion, we get sent out
to tackle looters raiding a bank.
And one of them legs it up the road,
probably armed, possibly not.

5   Well myself and somebody else and somebody else
are all of the same mind,
so all three of us open fire.
Three of a kind all letting fly, and I swear

I see every round as it rips through his life –
10   I see broad daylight on the other side.
So we've hit this looter a dozen times
and he's there on the ground, sort of inside out,

pain itself, the image of agony.
One of my mates goes by
15   and tosses his guts back into his body.
Then he's carted off in the back of a lorry.

End of story, except not really.
His blood-shadow stays on the street, and out on patrol
I walk right over it week after week.
20   Then I'm home on leave. But I blink

and he bursts again through the doors of the bank.
Sleep, and he's probably armed, possibly not.
Dream, and he's torn apart by a dozen rounds.
And the drink and the drugs won't flush him out –

25   he's here in my head when I close my eyes,
dug in behind enemy lines,
not left for dead in some distant, sun-stunned, sand-smothered land
or six-feet-under in desert sand,

but near to the knuckle, here and now,
30   his bloody life in my bloody hands.

Simon Armitage

Q1   Why do you think the speaker can't forget about the looter's death?

....

....

Q2   Explain the effect of the speaker changing from using "**we**" to "**I**" in line 8.

....

....

....

Q3 Find a quote that demonstrates each of the following techniques.
In each case, briefly explain the effect of the technique on the reader.

Technique	Quote	Effect
Repetition		
Colloquial language		

Q4 What effect is created through the short words and caesurae used in lines 22-23?

....

....

....

Q5 Find a quote that addresses each of the following feelings. Explain your choices.

a) Nonchalance

Quote: ....

Explanation: ....

....

b) Guilt

Quote: ....

Explanation: ....

....

Q6 What impression do you think the poet is trying to achieve by describing
the soldier's memory of the looter as "**dug in behind enemy lines**" (line 26)?

....

....

....

COMPARE POEMS

All that remains now is to crack on with your revision...

Read 'Exposure' by Wilfred Owen, on page 12, and compare it with 'Remains'.

- How do the poets present the effects of conflict on the speakers of each poem?
- How is form used to emphasise these effects?

Poppies

Three days before Armistice Sunday
and poppies had already been placed
on individual war graves. Before you left,
I pinned one onto your lapel, crimped petals,
5   spasms of paper red, disrupting a blockade
of yellow bias binding around your blazer.

Sellotape bandaged around my hand,
I rounded up as many white cat hairs
as I could, smoothed down your shirt's
10   upturned collar, steeled the softening
of my face. I wanted to graze my nose
across the tip of your nose, play at
being Eskimos like we did when
you were little. I resisted the impulse
15   to run my fingers through the gelled
blackthorns of your hair. All my words
flattened, rolled, turned into felt,

slowly melting. I was brave, as I walked
with you, to the front door, threw
20   it open, the world overflowing
like a treasure chest. A split second
and you were away, intoxicated.
After you'd gone I went into your bedroom,
released a song bird from its cage.
25   Later a single dove flew from the pear tree,
and this is where it has led me,
skirting the church yard walls, my stomach busy
making tucks, darts, pleats, hat-less, without
a winter coat or reinforcements of scarf, gloves.

30   On reaching the top of the hill I traced
the inscriptions on the war memorial,
leaned against it like a wishbone.
The dove pulled freely against the sky,
an ornamental stitch. I listened, hoping to hear
35   your playground voice catching on the wind.

Jane Weir

Q1   What do you learn about the speaker from the first stanza?

....

....

Q2   Describe the effect created by the enjambment and caesurae in the second stanza.

....

....

....

Q3 What is the effect of the mother recounting her memories of her son's childhood? Give an example from the poem to support your answer.

....

....

....

....

Stefan was adamant
that he didn't need the
reinforcement of a scarf.

Q4 What do you think the following images in line 25 might symbolise?

a) "**a single dove**": ....

....

b) "**the pear tree**": ....

....

Q5 How does the use of sensory language (e.g. touch, hearing) help to convey the mother's emotions?

....

....

....

....

Q6 Find a quote that addresses each of the following themes and explain the effect of the quote.

Theme	Quote	Explanation
Fear		
Freedom		

Caesura — my favourite type of salad...

PERSONAL RESPONSE

'The Emigrée' by Carol Rumens (page 26) is another poem that deals with the feeling of loss.
- Compare how the two poems use childhood memories to create a sense of loss.
- Which of the two poems do you think is more successful in creating a sense of loss?

War Photographer

In his darkroom he is finally alone
with spools of suffering set out in ordered rows.
The only light is red and softly glows,
as though this were a church and he
5 a priest preparing to intone a Mass.
Belfast. Beirut. Phnom Penh. All flesh is grass.

He has a job to do. Solutions slop in trays
beneath his hands, which did not tremble then
though seem to now. Rural England. Home again
10 to ordinary pain which simple weather can dispel,
to fields which don't explode beneath the feet
of running children in a nightmare heat.

Something is happening. A stranger's features
faintly start to twist before his eyes,
15 a half-formed ghost. He remembers the cries
of this man's wife, how he sought approval
without words to do what someone must
and how the blood stained into foreign dust.

A hundred agonies in black and white
20 from which his editor will pick out five or six
for Sunday's supplement. The reader's eyeballs prick
with tears between the bath and pre-lunch beers.
From the aeroplane he stares impassively at where
he earns his living and they do not care.

Carol Ann Duffy

Q1   The poem changes in line 13. What does "**Something**" in this line refer to?

....

....

Q2   Why do you think the poet chose to use the following elements of form?

Regular rhyme scheme: ....

....

Enjambment: ....

....

Q3 Find a quote that demonstrates each of the following types of language.
In each case, briefly explain the effect of this type of language.

Type of Language	Quote	Effect
Religious imagery		
Emotive language		

Q4 What is the effect of setting the poem in a darkroom?

....

....

....

Q5 What do you think the phrase "**a half-formed ghost**" (line 15) suggests about the stranger?

....

....

Q6 Find an example of where the poem evokes the sounds of war. Explain how it does this.

Example: ....

Explanation: ....

....

Q7 Look at the last two lines of the poem. What might the poet be
trying to convey about the photographer's attitude to his job?

....

....

....

I feel like sitting alone in a dark room after reading that...

How does 'War Photographer' explore the responses of different people to conflict? In your answer, you should:
* Compare the duty of the photographer with the duty of a soldier.
* Consider what attitude the speaker thinks the general public might have in responding to foreign wars.

Tissue

Paper that lets the light
shine through, this
is what could alter things.
Paper thinned by age or touching,

5   the kind you find in well-used books,
the back of the Koran, where a hand
has written in the names and histories,
who was born to whom,

the height and weight, who
10 died where and how, on which sepia date,
pages smoothed and stroked and turned
transparent with attention.

If buildings were paper, I might
feel their drift, see how easily
15 they fall away on a sigh, a shift
in the direction of the wind.

Maps too. The sun shines through
their borderlines, the marks
that rivers make, roads,
20 railtracks, mountainfolds,

Fine slips from grocery shops
that say how much was sold
and what was paid by credit card
might fly our lives like paper kites.

25 An architect could use all this,
place layer over layer, luminous
script over numbers over line,
and never wish to build again with brick

or block, but let the daylight break
30 through capitals and monoliths,
through the shapes that pride can make,
find a way to trace a grand design

with living tissue, raise a structure
never meant to last,
35 of paper smoothed and stroked
and thinned to be transparent,

turned into your skin.

Imtiaz Dharker

Q1   Read the first stanza. How does the poet set the scene for the rest of the poem?

....

....

Q2   Find a quote to illustrate each of the following statements,
then briefly explain how the quote relates to the statement.

a) Light is portrayed as a positive force.

Quote: ....

Explanation: ....

b) Paper is treated with respect by humans.

Quote: ....

....

Explanation: ....

....

"You've just got to roll with it,"
said Ken to his unamused brother.

Q3 How does Dharker use the poem's form to explore the theme of freedom?

....

....

....

....

Q4 Find a quote which deals with each of the following themes and explain the effect of the quote.

Theme	Quote	Explanation
Control		
Fragility		

Q5 Why do you think Dharker chose to call the poem 'Tissue'?

....

....

....

Q6 Is everything in 'Tissue' presented as being temporary? Use evidence to support your answer.

....

....

....

....

....

'Tissue' — sounds like someone's got a cold coming on...

Read 'Checking Out Me History' by John Agard, on page 30, and compare it with 'Tissue'.
- What do the poems suggest about how human identity is formed?
- How are the poetic voices used to present ideas about identity?

Section One — The Poems

The Emigrée

There once was a country... I left it as a child
but my memory of it is sunlight-clear
for it seems I never saw it in that November
which, I am told, comes to the mildest city.
5   The worst news I receive of it cannot break
my original view, the bright, filled paperweight.
It may be at war, it may be sick with tyrants,
but I am branded by an impression of sunlight.

The white streets of that city, the graceful slopes
10 glow even clearer as time rolls its tanks
and the frontiers rise between us, close like waves.
That child's vocabulary I carried here
like a hollow doll, opens and spills a grammar.
Soon I shall have every coloured molecule of it.
15 It may by now be a lie, banned by the state
but I can't get it off my tongue. It tastes of sunlight.

I have no passport, there's no way back at all
but my city comes to me in its own white plane.
It lies down in front of me, docile as paper;
20 I comb its hair and love its shining eyes.
My city takes me dancing through the city
of walls. They accuse me of absence, they circle me.
They accuse me of being dark in their free city.
My city hides behind me. They mutter death,
25 and my shadow falls as evidence of sunlight.

Carol Rumens

Q1   What do you learn about the speaker from the opening stanza?

....

....

Q2   Find two examples of personification, then say what effect each has.

Quote: ....

Effect: ....

....

Quote: ....

Effect: ....

....

Section One — The Poems

Q3 Compare the enjambment used in the first two stanzas to the end-stopping in the final stanza. What effect do these features have?

....

....

Q4 What does the line "**but I am branded by an impression of sunlight**" (line 8) suggest about the speaker?

....

....

Q5 How does the language used in the poem create a vivid description of the speaker's former city? Use evidence to support your answer.

....

....

....

....

Q6 How does Rumens use language to present the speaker as an outcast?

....

....

....

....

Billy couldn't understand why
no one ever took him dancing.

Q7 Read the last two lines of the poem. What do they suggest about the speaker?

....

....

....

....

Tasting sunlight — one of your five a day...

How does the poem explore the theme of conflict? Write a couple of paragraphs which cover the following:

* The language used to portray the speaker's former city — particularly the language used in line 7.
* The speaker's experiences of feeling threatened in her new city, as seen in the final stanza.

Kamikaze

Her father embarked at sunrise
with a flask of water, a samurai sword
in the cockpit, a shaven head
full of powerful incantations
5 and enough fuel for a one-way
journey into history

but half way there, she thought,
recounting it later to her children,
he must have looked far down
10 at the little fishing boats
strung out like bunting
on a green-blue translucent sea

and beneath them, arcing in swathes
like a huge flag waved first one way
15 then the other in a figure of eight,
the dark shoals of fishes
flashing silver as their bellies
swivelled towards the sun

and remembered how he
20 and his brothers waiting on the shore
built cairns of pearl-grey pebbles
to see whose withstood longest
the turbulent inrush of breakers
bringing their father's boat safe

25 – yes, grandfather's boat – safe
to the shore, salt-sodden, awash
with cloud-marked mackerel,
black crabs, feathery prawns,
the loose silver of whitebait and once
30 a tuna, the dark prince, muscular, dangerous.

And though he came back
my mother never spoke again
in his presence, nor did she meet his eyes
and the neighbours too, they treated him
35 *as though he no longer existed,*
only we children still chattered and laughed

till gradually we too learned
to be silent, to live as though
he had never returned, that this
40 *was no longer the father we loved.*
And sometimes, she said, he must have wondered
which had been the better way to die.

Beatrice Garland

Q1 Look at the following phrases from the first stanza.
What might they reveal about kamikaze pilots?

   a) "**a shaven head / full of powerful incantations**" (lines 3-4)

   ....

   ....

   b) "**enough fuel for a one-way / journey into history**" (lines 5-6)

   ....

   ....

Q2 What effect do the following elements of form in the poem have?

   Lack of pilot's voice: ....

   ....

   Direct speech from daughter: ....

   ....

Q3 Find two examples of natural imagery, then say what the effect of each one is.

Imagery of nature quote	Effect

Q4 What role do childhood memories play in the poem?

....

....

....

....

Q5 Find a quote that deals with each of the following feelings. Explain your choices.

a) Regret

Quote: ....

Explanation: ....

....

b) Shame

Quote: ....

Explanation: ....

....

Q6 Do you sympathise with the pilot's daughter? Explain your answer using evidence from the text.

....

....

....

I'll have a dark prince and mayo on granary please...

'The Charge of the Light Brigade', by Alfred Tennyson (page 10), also features a sense of patriotism.
- How do both poets present soldiers' reactions to patriotism in a conflict setting?
- Which poem do you think questions the worth of patriotism the most? Explain your answer.

Checking Out Me History

Dem tell me
Dem tell me
Wha dem want to tell me

5   Bandage up me eye with me own history
Blind me to me own identity

Dem tell me bout 1066 and all dat
dem tell me bout Dick Whittington and he cat
But Toussaint L'Ouverture
no dem never tell me bout dat

10   *Toussaint*
a slave
with vision
lick back
Napoleon
15   *battalion*
and first Black
Republic born
Toussaint de thorn
to de French
20   *Toussaint de beacon*
of de Haitian Revolution

Dem tell me bout de man who discover de balloon
and de cow who jump over de moon
Dem tell me bout de dish ran away with de spoon
25   but dem never tell me bout Nanny de maroon

Nanny
see-far woman
of mountain dream
fire-woman struggle
30   *hopeful stream*
to freedom river

Dem tell me bout Lord Nelson and Waterloo
but dem never tell me bout Shaka de great Zulu
Dem tell me bout Columbus and 1492
35   but what happen to de Caribs and de Arawaks too

Dem tell me bout Florence Nightingale and she lamp
and how Robin Hood used to camp
Dem tell me bout ole King Cole was a merry ole soul
but dem never tell me bout Mary Seacole

40   *From Jamaica*
she travel far
to the Crimean War
she volunteer to go
and even when de British said no
45   *she still brave the Russian snow*
a healing star
among the wounded
a yellow sunrise
to the dying

50   Dem tell me
Dem tell me wha dem want to tell me
But now I checking out me own history
I carving out me identity

John Agard

Q1   What do you learn about the speaker from the first stanza?

....

....

....

Waterloo this is...

Q2   Why does the poet choose to use phonetic spellings, e.g. "**dem**" and "**de**", in the poem?

....

....

....

Section One — The Poems

Q3 Find a quote which demonstrates each of the following feelings.
In each case, explain how the quote presents this feeling.

Feeling	Quote	Explanation
Anger		
Admiration		
Celebration		

Q4 Look at the following elements of form. How is a contrast between
British and Caribbean history created through these in the poem?

Stanza forms: ....

....

....

Sentence structure: ....

....

....

Q5 What is the effect of Agard's use of imagery relating to
vision and blindness? Use examples in your answer.

....

....

....

....

....

Dem tell me: wash the dishes, clean your room — sigh...

COMPARE POEMS

Read 'London' by William Blake, on page 4, and compare it with 'Checking Out Me History'.
• Who or what are the speakers in each poem angry at?
• How is their anger presented in the poems?

Using Quotes

In the exam, you'll need to support your points with quotes from the poems, especially when you're analysing language. You'll only get a copy of the named poem in the exam, so you need to memorise some key quotes to use in your answer. It's important to keep the quotes short and relevant.

Embedding quotes will impress the examiner. This just means inserting them as if they're a natural part of the sentence — e.g. 'The pilot was treated "as though he no longer existed" after he returned.'

Q1 For each of the following, underline the part of the quote that best supports the point.

   a) The experience described in 'Exposure' is a collective one.

> "Slowly our ghosts drag home: glimpsing the sunk fires"

   b) The narrator of 'Tissue' describes how human structures are only temporary.

> "If buildings were paper, I might / feel their drift, see how easily / they fall away on a sigh, a shift / in the direction of the wind."

Q2 Pick out a suitable quote to illustrate each of the following points.

   a) The narrator of 'Poppies' feels cut off from her son.

   ....

   b) 'Remains' has an anecdotal tone.

   ....

Q3 Read the following extract from a sample answer:

> In 'The Prelude', Wordsworth emphasises how confident the narrator feels while he is rowing the boat — "like one who rows, / Proud of his skill, to reach a chosen point / With an unswerving line" — although this confidence could be perceived as arrogance. Similarly, the Duke in 'My Last Duchess' is proud of his heritage — "My gift of a nine-hundred-years-old name" — his pride also borders on arrogance as he boasts about his family's status.

Rewrite the extract, embedding and improving the use of quotes.

....

....

....

....

P.E.E.D.

To get a good mark, you're going to have to explain and develop any points and examples you use. Using **P.E.E.D.** is a great way to structure your paragraphs so that you include everything you need.

For each **point**, provide a quote or **example** from the poem and **explain** how this supports your point. Then, you need to **develop** your point by commenting on the effect it has on the reader, linking it with another part of the poem, relating it to the poem's context or comparing it with the other poem.

Q1 The following sample answer extracts haven't used P.E.E.D. correctly. For each, say which stage of P.E.E.D. is missing, then write a sentence you could include to improve the extract.

a)

> In 'The Emigrée', there are different levels of distance between the narrator and the country she left behind. She is geographically distant from the country, but she still has a close emotional connection to it. Here, Rumens seems to be implying that even if we experience loss, there is the potential for comfort in the memories we keep.

Missing stage: .... Addition: ....

....

....

b)

> In 'Bayonet Charge', Hughes suggests that patriotism is not what drives soldiers forwards in battle. The soldier is described as dropping "King, honour, human dignity, etcetera" as though they were "luxuries". This mirrors the first stanza, where the soldier's "patriotic tear" is replaced by "molten iron", showing that patriotism is vulnerable to being abandoned.

Missing stage: .... Addition: ....

....

....

Q2 Sometimes you can make a development point for both poems at the same time. Write a development point that does this for the following paragraph.

> Physical objects are used to symbolise power in both 'Ozymandias' and 'Tissue'. In 'Ozymandias', the statue's inscription invites other rulers to "despair" as they look at his "works". This shows how Ozymandias uses the statue as a symbol of his might. In 'Tissue', paper is presented as a powerful object that allows humans to record information about their "names and histories". In this way, paper can be seen to symbolise the power of human identity and how it consists of many aspects.

Development: ....

....

....

Section Two — Themes

Power of Humans

Q1 Find a quote from the following poems which questions the way in which the authorities have used their power, then explain how each quote shows this.

a) 'London'

Quote: ....

Explanation: ....

....

b) 'Checking Out Me History'

Quote: ....

Explanation: ....

....

Q2 How does the dramatic monologue form used in 'My Last Duchess' emphasise the Duke's power?

....

....

....

Q3 Describe how Dharker explores the fragility of human power in 'Tissue'.

....

....

....

Q4 What does the phrase "**sneer of cold command**" in line 5 of 'Ozymandias' suggest about Ozymandias's power?

....

....

....

EXAM PRACTICE

Try this practice question to get into the swing of things...

In 'London', Blake explores ideas about people who misuse their power. How is the theme of human power presented in 'London' and one other poem from 'Power and Conflict'? **[30 marks]**

Power of Nature

Q1 In 'Kamikaze', do you think nature was the most influential factor in the pilot's decision to turn around, or was it something else? Give reasons to support your answer.

....

....

....

Q2 How does the poet use language to present nature as a powerful force in 'Storm on the Island'?

....

....

....

....

Q3 Which is presented as a more powerful force in 'Ozymandias', humans or nature? Explain your answer.

....

....

....

....

With wrinkled lips, Max sneered at the power of nature.

Q4 Compare how nature is depicted as an enemy in 'Exposure' and 'The Prelude'. Which do you find is the most effective poem at conveying nature as dangerous?

....

....

....

....

....

EXAM TIP

Consider the impact that imagery has on the reader...

Poets use imagery to invoke emotions or a reaction in the reader — consider what these might be and comment on their effect. E.g. do you feel inspired or terrified by the natural imagery in 'The Prelude'?

Effects of Conflict

Q1 How has war affected the soldiers' perception of home in 'Exposure'?

....

....

....

....

Q2 Compare how the psychological effects of war are
presented in 'Remains' and 'War Photographer'.

....

....

....

....

Q3 How does Tennyson emphasise the human cost of war in 'The Charge of the Light Brigade'?

....

....

....

....

Q4 Compare the effects conflict has on families in 'Poppies' and 'Kamikaze'.

....

....

....

....

Analyse the techniques used to create effects...

In 'Bayonet Charge', Hughes explores the devastating effects of conflict. How are the effects of
conflict presented in 'Bayonet Charge' and one other poem from 'Power and Conflict'? **[30 marks]**

Reality of Conflict

Q1 Explain the role sound has in conveying the reality of war in 'The Charge of the Light Brigade'.

....

....

....

....

Q2 Choose one poem that describes conflict as it happens and one that describes it after the event. Then consider the effect of the poet choosing to set the poem at this time.

Perspective	Poem	Effect of Perspective
As it happens		
After the event		

Q3 How does Owen use imagery to present conflict as horrifying in 'Exposure'?

....

....

....

....

Q4 How is the soldier presented as a victim of conflict in 'Bayonet Charge'?

....

....

....

....

Think how the speaker's perspective affects the poem...

EXAM TIP

First-person and third-person narrators allow poets to present different perspectives of conflict. For example, the use of a first-person perspective in 'Remains' intensifies the horror of the looter's death.

Loss and Absence

Q1 What do you think is the narrator's opinion of the loss of life he describes in 'The Charge of the Light Brigade'? Consider the poem's context in your answer.

....

....

....

Q2 Find a quote in 'The Emigrée' that suggests how the speaker deals with her absence from her former city. Explain how it does this.

Quote: ....

Explanation: ....

....

....

Q3 In 'My Last Duchess', what do you think of the Duke's emotions regarding his former wife? Does he show any sense of loss?

....

....

....

....

Q4 "The total absence of hope in 'London' and 'Exposure' comes from the fact that those suffering are unable to change their situations." Discuss this statement.

....

....

....

....

....

Using P.E.E.D. will help to structure your answer...

'Kamikaze' explores the loss of a family member as a consequence of war. Compare how personal loss is presented in 'Kamikaze' and one other poem from 'Power and Conflict'. **[30 marks]**

Section Two — Themes

Memory

Q1 What do you think is the relationship between the title and the theme of memory in 'Poppies'?

....

....

....

Q2 In 'The Emigrée', do you think the speaker's memories of the city she left are reliable? Explain your answer.

....

....

....

....

....

Q3 In 'War Photographer', what do you think Duffy is trying to convey by having the photographer's hands "**tremble**" (line 8) as he develops the photo?

....

....

....

Q4 Read lines 33-44 of 'The Prelude'. Explain how the speaker's memory of the mountain affects him.

....

....

....

....

....

Give your own interpretations whenever you can...

EXAM TIP

You might think the narrator in 'London' is unreliable or that 'The Emigrée' is about the transition to adulthood. The examiner will be impressed by an interpretation of a poem, but only if you back it up.

Negative Emotions

Q1 Do you think the photographer in 'War Photographer' feels guilty? Explain your answer.

....

....

....

Q2 How is the soldier in 'Remains' presented as feeling personally responsible for the looter's death?

....

....

....

....

Q3 How does the language in 'Bayonet Charge' give
the impression that the soldier feels out of control?

....

....

....

....

....

Q4 Compare the shifts in emotion that occur in 'The Prelude' and 'Storm on the Island'.

....

....

....

....

....

Always spend time planning your answer...

After her son leaves home to join the army, the mother in 'Poppies' experiences fear. How is the
feeling of fear presented in 'Poppies' and one other poem from 'Power and Conflict'? **[30 marks]**

Identity

Q1 Find a quote from 'Poppies' which shows the mother is still attached to her son's identity as a boy rather than a soldier. Explain how it shows this.

Quote: ....

....

Explanation: ....

....

Geoff hit rock bottom when he started to identify as a goblin.

Q2 In 'Tissue', what do you think the phrase "**living tissue [...] turned into your skin**" (lines 33 and 37) suggests about human identity?

....

....

....

Q3 Assess the importance of identity to the pilot in 'Kamikaze'. Consider both personal and national identity in your answer.

....

....

....

....

Q4 Using examples from the text, explain how the speaker in 'Checking Out Me History' feels that his identity has been neglected.

....

....

....

....

....

EXAM TIP

Jot down some key quotes when planning your answer...

Spend some time picking out key quotes for each poem. You'll only get a copy of the named poem in the exam, so make sure you get some quotes learnt — this will make it all much easier on the day.

Individual Experiences

Q1 In 'War Photographer', how is the photographer presented as being separate from the rest of society?

....

....

....

Q2 How does the form of 'The Emigrée' give the feeling that this is a personal poem?

....

....

....

....

Q3 In 'Bayonet Charge', the poet uses an image of a single "**yellow hare**" (line 16). Explain how this image might reflect the soldier's experience on the battlefield.

....

....

....

....

....

Q4 In 'London', how is the narrator's separation from the city presented? What is the effect of this separation?

....

....

....

....

Don't treat the poet and the speaker as the same person...

The speaker in 'The Prelude' feels isolated after encountering the mountain. Compare the presentation of negative experiences in 'The Prelude' and one other poem from 'Power and Conflict'. **[30 marks]**

☹ ☐   ☺ ☐   ☺ ☐

Discussing Context

Writing about the context of the poems is an essential part of an exam answer. Have a think about when and where each poem was set and how the ideas in the poem relate to that time and place. You could also mention whether the poet comments on society, draws on aspects of their background or culture, or if they were influenced by other works of literature or any literary movements.

Have a go at the questions below to start thinking about context and how to use it in your exam.

Q1 Read these sample answer extracts and underline any contextual information.

a)

Heaney uses violent, war-like imagery in 'Storm on the Island'. Words such as "strafes" and "bombarded" create a hostile environment as though the island is under attack from enemy fire. The "Storm" may be a reference to political disturbances in Heaney's home country of Northern Ireland. The first eight letters of the poem's title spell out 'Stormont', which is the name of the parliament buildings in Northern Ireland, and so the "Storm" could refer to the violence between Irish republicans and unionists.

b)

In the final line of 'Remains', the narrator says that he has the looter's "bloody life" in his "bloody hands." This could be the narrator swearing in anger at the situation, but it could also be seen as a sign of his guilt. The reference to "bloody hands" may be an allusion to Shakespeare's *Macbeth*, as after persuading her husband to murder King Duncan, Lady Macbeth tries to wash imaginary blood off her hands while she sleepwalks. The allusion to this image emphasises the narrator's guilty, perhaps even unbalanced state of mind.

c)

There are significant indications in 'My Last Duchess' that the Duke has had his Duchess murdered. Descriptions of the Duchess such as the "Half-flush that dies along her throat" contribute to a sense of suspicion in the poem — the reference to death in this line feels out of place and the reader questions this choice of word. This sense is further emphasised by the poem's setting of "*Ferrara*", as the sixteenth-century Duke of Ferrara's wife, Lucrezia, died in suspicious circumstances and was rumoured to have been poisoned.

Q2 Read the following sample answer extract.

Nature is shown to be more powerful than humans in both 'The Prelude' and 'Exposure'. The mountain in 'The Prelude' grows "in stature" as the speaker tries to escape it, making his experience of nature sound like a nightmare. Similarly, in 'Exposure', the soldiers' brains "ache", showing the harrowing effect nature has had both physically and psychologically.

Write a development point that refers to the context of one or both of the poems.

....

....

....

....

Section Three — Poetic Techniques

Forms of Poetry

Q1 What can you infer about the narrator of 'The Emigrée' from the form of the poem?

....

....

Q2 Why do you think Owen chose to impose such a rigid form on his poem 'Exposure'?

....

....

Q3 How does the form of 'Remains' reflect the narrator's state of mind following the shooting?

....

....

....

Q4 In 'Ozymandias', how does Shelley use the sonnet form to comment on human power?

....

....

....

....

Ben was starting to reconsider just how powerful he felt.

Q5 Compare the form of 'The Charge of the Light Brigade' with that of 'Bayonet Charge'. In what ways do the forms of the poems affect how they present the reality of conflict?

....

....

....

....

....

EXAM TIP

Always comment on the form of the poem...

A poet's use of form (rhyme scheme, line lengths, metre etc.) is just as important as their language. Most of the time these work together to convey the poet's message, so you need to discuss them both.

Poetic Devices

Q1 What does the repetition of **"safe"** in 'Kamikaze' (lines 24-25)
suggest about the pilot in that moment?

....

....

Q2 Explain the effect of each of the following examples of sensory language.

Poem	Quote	Effect of sensory language
'London'	"In every cry of every man, / In every infant's cry of fear, / In every voice, in every ban, / The mind-forged manacles I hear." (lines 5-8)	
'Remains'	"I see every round as it rips through his life – / I see broad daylight on the other side." (lines 9-10)	

Q3 What is the effect of the end-stopping in the opening two lines of 'Storm on the Island'?

....

....

Q4 How does Wordsworth use contrast to emphasise the narrator's fear in 'The Prelude'?

....

....

....

Q5 Find an example of irony in 'Checking Out Me History' and explain its effect.

Example: ....

Effect: ....

....

Give this question a go — they say practice makes perfect...

EXAM PRACTICE

Poetic devices can be used to reinforce a poem's themes. Compare the ways in which loss is portrayed
in 'The Charge of the Light Brigade' and one other poem from 'Power and Conflict'. **[30 marks]**

Use of Sound

Q1 For each quote below, comment on the effect created by the use of sound.

   a) 'War Photographer': "**pick out five or six / for Sunday's supplement.**" (lines 20-21)

   ....

   ....

   b) 'Ozymandias': "**boundless and bare / The lone and level sands stretch far away.**" (lines 13-14)

   ....

   ....

Q2 How does Dharker's use of alliteration in 'Tissue' affect the tone of the poem?

   ....

   ....

Q3 In 'The Prelude', what is the effect of sound in the phrase "**I struck and struck again**" (line 24)?

   ....

   ....

Q4 Find a quote from 'Bayonet Charge' which mimics the sounds of battle. Explain your choice.

   Quote: ....

   Explanation: ....

   ....

Q5 In which poem do you think the use of sound is more effective —
   'Storm on the Island' or 'Exposure'? Explain your answer.

   ....

   ....

   ....

   ....

EXAM TIP

Reading the poems aloud can help you identify sounds...

Obviously you can't give a dramatic reading of the poems in the middle of your exam, but by reading them aloud beforehand, it will make it much easier for you to spot the sounds again on the day.

Section Three — Poetic Techniques

Imagery

Q1 For each of the following, give an example of the technique and explain its effect.

a) Personification in 'The Charge of the Light Brigade'

Personification: ....

Effect: ....

....

b) A metaphor in 'War Photographer'

Metaphor: ....

Effect: ....

....

Q2 How does the mixture of military and domestic imagery in 'Poppies' convey the reality of conflict?

....

....

Q3 How does the imagery of layers in 'Tissue' contribute to the overall message of the poem?

....

....

....

Q4 "The imagery in 'Remains' suggests that the narrator has become desensitised to violence." To what extent do you agree with this statement? Explain your answer.

....

....

....

....

Write about the effect of any imagery you pick out...

EXAM PRACTICE

In her poem 'Tissue', Dharker compares the power of nature and human constructs. Compare the presentation of nature in 'Tissue' and one other poem from 'Power and Conflict'. **[30 marks]**

Rhyme and Rhythm

Q1 Give an example of a half-rhyme from 'Exposure'
and explain the effect half-rhymes have in the poem.

Example: ....

Effect: ....

....

....

....

What the group lacked in
rhythm, they sure made
up for in coordination.

Q2 What rhythm does Browning use in 'My Last Duchess'? Explain the effect it has.

....

....

....

Q3 Why do you think Agard creates chant-like rhythms in
the Caribbean stanzas of 'Checking Out Me History'?

....

....

....

....

Q4 What effect does the lack of rhyme in 'Remains' and 'Poppies' have on
the tone of the poems? Is the effect similar or different in each poem?

....

....

....

....

Section Three — Poetic Techniques

Voice

Q1 How does the first-person voice in 'London' affect how the city is presented?

....

....

Q2 Why do you think Garland uses the voice of the pilot's daughter instead of the pilot in 'Kamikaze'?

....

....

Q3 What do the lines **"for it seems I never saw it in that November / which, I am told, comes to the mildest city."** (lines 3-4) suggest about the voice of 'The Emigrée'?

....

....

....

Q4 In 'My Last Duchess', how does Browning use the voice of the Duke to set a sinister tone?

....

....

....

....

Q5 How is the voice in 'War Photographer' different from the voice in 'Exposure'? How do these differences affect how the reality of war is conveyed?

....

....

....

....

....

Sometimes a voice can change throughout the poem...

A change in voice can affect the message of a poem. Compare how voice is used to explore ideas about conflict in 'Checking Out Me History' and one other poem from 'Power and Conflict'. **[30 marks]**

Beginnings of Poems

Q1   What is the effect of each of the following opening lines?

Poem	Opening line	Effect
'Ozymandias'	"I met a traveller from an antique land"	
'My Last Duchess'	"That's my last Duchess painted on the wall,"	

Q2   What does the first line of 'War Photographer', "**In his darkroom he is finally alone**", suggest about how the photographer feels in the darkroom?

....

....

....

Q3   Is the tone of the first stanza in 'Kamikaze' representative of the poem as a whole? Explain your answer.

....

....

....

Q4   How can you tell just from their opening stanzas that 'The Charge of the Light Brigade' and 'Remains' present conflict in different ways?

....

....

....

....

....

If you're stuck, comment on the beginning of the poem...

Beginnings have an important job to do — they set the tone, try to capture the reader's attention and may establish the poem's message. Happily, this means there will usually be something there to analyse.

Endings of Poems

Q1 What is the effect of each of the following closing lines?

Poem	Closing line	Effect
'Tissue'	"turned into your skin."	
'Ozymandias'	"The lone and level sands stretch far away."	
'Storm on the Island'	"Strange, it is a huge nothing that we fear."	

Q2 What does the final line of 'Bayonet Charge', "**His terror's touchy dynamite.**", suggest about the soldier?

....

....

Q3 What is the effect of the final line, "**And blights with plagues the marriage hearse.**", in 'London'?

....

....

....

Q4 In what ways do the final five lines of 'The Prelude' emphasise how the narrator's mindset has changed since the first five lines of the extract?

....

....

....

EXAM TIP

Compare the endings with the beginnings of poems...

By looking at how the poem has changed between the first and final lines, you can see how themes, ideas and feelings have been developed, as well as how the tone, voice and mood may have changed.

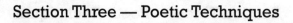

Mood

Q1 Describe the mood created by each of the following quotes.

Poem	Quote	Mood
'War Photographer'	"as though this were a church and he / a priest preparing to intone a Mass." (lines 4-5)	
'The Emigrée'	"my shadow falls as evidence of sunlight." (line 25)	

Q2 How does the rhythm of 'The Charge of the Light Brigade' contribute to the mood of the poem?

....

....

Q3 What is the mood in the final stanza of 'Checking Out Me History'?
How does this differ from the mood in the first stanza?

....

....

....

....

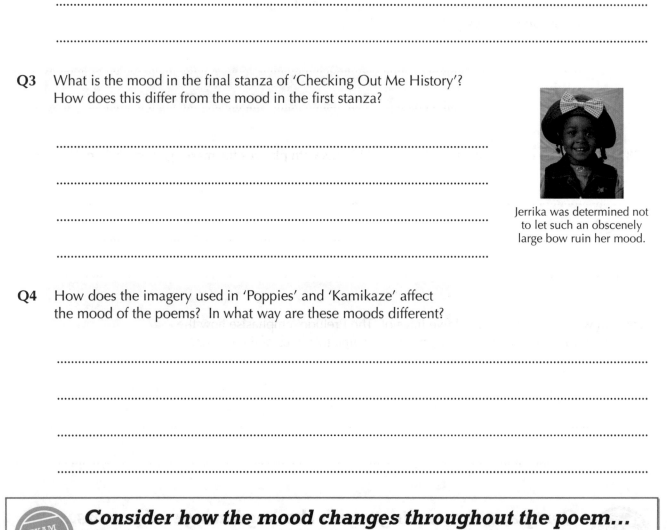

Jerrika was determined not to let such an obscenely large bow ruin her mood.

Q4 How does the imagery used in 'Poppies' and 'Kamikaze' affect the mood of the poems? In what way are these moods different?

....

....

....

....

EXAM PRACTICE

Consider how the mood changes throughout the poem...

If there's a turning point in a poem, there may be change of mood too. Compare the ways in which mood is used to present conflict in 'Remains' and one other poem from 'Power and Conflict'. **[30 marks]**

Analysing Language, Structure and Form

SKILLS
FOCUS

There's no escaping it — you simply have to write about language, structure and form. Think about any poetic techniques the poet has used, how they've structured their ideas, and what effect the form of the poem has — this includes the rhythm, rhyme scheme, metre, line lengths and voice.

It's not enough to just pick out these techniques — you need to explain what effect they have and discuss how they might make the reader feel. Hone your skills by answering the question below.

Q1 Read the following extract from John Agard's poem 'Checking Out Me History'.

	Dem tell me	10	*Toussaint*
	Dem tell me		*a slave*
	Wha dem want to tell me		*with vision*
			lick back
	Bandage up me eye with me own history		*Napoleon*
5	Blind me to me own identity	15	*battalion*
			and first Black
	Dem tell me bout 1066 and all dat		*Republic born*
	dem tell me bout Dick Whittington and he cat		*Toussaint de thorn*
	But Toussaint L'Ouverture		*to de French*
	no dem never tell me bout dat	20	*Toussaint de beacon*
			of de Haitian Revolution

Analyse the effect of each of the following in the extract:

a) Language

....

....

....

b) Structure

....

....

....

c) Form

....

....

....

Planning Your Answer

Read the question carefully and underline key words

Q1   Read the following questions then underline what you think are the most important words.

   a)   Compare the presentation of conflict in 'Bayonet Charge'
          and one other poem from 'Power and Conflict'.

   b)   Compare how the theme of memory is presented in 'Kamikaze'
          and one other poem from 'Power and Conflict'.

   c)   Compare how ideas about identity are explored in 'Checking Out Me History'
          and one other poem from 'Power and Conflict'.

Decide on the second poem to use in your comparison

Q2   For each question below, choose the second poem you might use and explain your choice.

   a)   How is the theme of nature explored in 'The Prelude: Stealing the Boat'
          and one other poem from 'Power and Conflict'?

   Poem: ....

   Explanation: ....

   ....

   ....

   b)   Compare how the effects of conflict are presented in 'Remains'
          and one other poem from 'Power and Conflict'.

   Poem: ....

   Explanation: ....

   ....

   ....

   c)   Explore the ways arrogance is presented in 'My Last Duchess'
          and one other poem from 'Power and Conflict'.

   Poem: ....

   Explanation: ....

   ....

   ....

Planning Your Answer

Jot down your main ideas

Q3 Look at the exam question in Q1 a) on p.54 and choose the second poem you'd use to answer it. Then fill in the plan below with three main points comparing the poems.

(Introduction)

Point One: ....

....

Point Two: ....

....

Point Three: ....

....

(Conclusion)

Pick out some key quotes and examples for your plan

Q4 Fill in the table below with relevant quotes or examples for the points you chose in Q3.

Evidence	'Bayonet Charge'	Chosen Poem
Evidence for Point One		
Evidence for Point Two		
Evidence for Point Three		

Na na na na na na na na na na na na na na na na — jot a plan!

A plan will be your only company in the exam, so you should always make one. It'll help you to stay focused on the question and to structure your essay nicely. Don't spend longer than about 5 minutes planning though.

Comparing Poems

Use linking words for an effective comparison

Q1 Use the linking words from the box to fill in the gaps in these
sentences and create comparisons between the two poems.

	furthermore	in contrast
likewise		whereas
	similarly	in the same way

a) Cultural identity is explored in 'Checking Out Me History', ... 'Poppies'
deals with the theme of family identity.

b) Owen uses a regular rhyme scheme in 'Exposure'. .... , Armitage's
'Remains' has no fixed rhyme scheme.

c) The Duke in 'My Last Duchess' appears to have absolute control, and in 'Ozymandias'
Shelley presents Ozymandias as a .... authoritarian figure.

Describe similarities and differences in your analysis

Q2 Improve the following paragraph so that it makes a more effective comparison between
the two poems. Add in linking words or phrases and rewrite any bits that you need to.

> 'Remains' shows how guilt affects a soldier involved in conflict. The figurative language in
> "he's here in my head" shows how the soldier's guilt over killing the looter mentally disturbs
> him, as if he can't escape it. The photographer in 'War Photographer' is disturbed by his feeling
> of guilt. The reference to "ordinary pain which simple weather can dispel" hints that he feels
> guilty about how comfortable life is in England. He seems to only be affected by this guilt after
> returning home. The soldier in 'Remains' isn't affected by guilt until he is home on leave.

....

....

....

....

....

....

Shall I compare thee to a — wait, no, that's not in the anthology...

A big chunk of the marks for the 'Power and Conflict' question are awarded for showing you've made an effective
comparison supported by examples and quotes. Just remember to compare the poems throughout your answer.

Structuring Your Answer

P.E.E.D. stands for Point, Example, Explain, Develop

Q1 Read the following extract from an exam answer. Label each aspect of P.E.E.D. — some of the aspects are used more than once.

> Both 'Exposure' and 'Storm on the Island' present nature as a dangerous force. In 'Exposure', the winds "knive" the soldiers, with the personification giving the impression that nature is attacking the men. Similarly, in 'Storm on the Island', the islanders are "bombarded" by the storm, creating the image of a bomber plane besieging the island. Comparing the weather to weapons heightens the threat that nature poses to the characters in each poem.

Embed quotes in your answer

Q2 Rewrite the following sentences so that a short part of the quote is embedded in each one.

a) The islanders in 'Storm on the Island' feel ready for the storm. — "We are prepared"

....

b) In 'The Emigrée', the speaker's city appears to her. — "It lies down in front of me"

....

Structure each paragraph using the P.E.E.D. method

Q3 In note form, use P.E.E.D. to structure a paragraph on your first point from Q3 on page 55.

Point: ....

....

Example (Poem 1): ....

Explain (Poem 1): ....

Example (Poem 2): ....

Explain (Poem 2): ....

Develop: ....

....

Go on, have a laugh — get it all out of your system...

P.E.E.D. actually serves a purpose beyond making people giggle — it's really useful for structuring your arguments and picking up marks. Using P.E.E.D. can be tricky at first, but stick with it and you'll soon get the hang of it.

Introductions and Conclusions

Present a clear answer to the question in your introduction

Q1 Look at the exam question in Q1 on p.59. Tick the boxes which you think should be included in an introduction to this question.

a) An analysis of each poem's opening line. ☐

b) A detailed discussion of each poem's form. ☐

c) Some of the answer's main ideas. ☐

d) Several quotes from each poem. ☐

e) A direct response to the question. ☐

Summarise your main points in your conclusion

Q2 Decide which of the following conclusions you think is better, then explain why.

> **a)** 'Bayonet Charge' presents a vivid depiction of the terror the soldier experiences during conflict. The soldier being described as "terror's touchy dynamite" could reflect how his fear has reduced him to a weapon which could explode at any point. Throughout the poem, Hughes seems overtly critical of conflict and questions the importance of patriotism. In 'Exposure', Owen also questions the worth of war and patriotism by presenting the horrible suffering of the soldiers in the trenches. As a result of graphic images such as "All their eyes are ice", the reader can empathise with the soldiers' struggle, as this image allows the reader to share in their suffering.

> **b)** Both Hughes and Owen effectively capture the feeling of hopelessness experienced by the soldiers in the trenches, despite Hughes's poem being written around forty years later. Through the violent, graphic imagery, sound devices and voice in each poem, the poets successfully instil a sense of the horrors of war in the reader's mind. For this reason, the poems can be seen as subtle criticisms of more traditional war poetry, which would often glorify and idealise the idea of dying for your country. Where they differ is that, while the soldiers in 'Exposure' feel hopeless when faced with the relentless weather, the soldier in 'Bayonet Charge' feels insignificant because he is isolated on the battlefield.

Better Conclusion: .... **Explanation:** ....

....

....

....

As my Gran always says, don't be afraid to introduce yourself...

Just like a fine piece of art, you're going to want to frame your essay. A good introduction which presents your ideas and a conclusion which summarises them will let the examiner behold your masterpiece in all its glory...

Marking Sample Answers

Get familiar with the mark scheme

Grade band	An answer at this level...
8-9	• Shows an insightful and original comparison of the two poems • Effectively integrates a full range of precise examples to support interpretations • Closely analyses the poets' use of language, structure and form, making effective use of technical terms throughout • Gives a detailed exploration of how the poets' techniques affect the reader • Convincingly explores original and alternative interpretations of the ideas, themes, attitudes and context of the poems
6-7	• Presents a carefully thought out, developed comparison of the two poems • Integrates well-chosen examples to support interpretations • Explores the poets' use of language, structure and form, using correct technical terms • Examines the way the techniques used in the poems affect the reader • Gives careful consideration to the ideas, themes, attitudes and/or context of the poems, offering some original interpretations
4-5	• Gives a clear comparison of the two poems • Provides relevant detail to support interpretations of the poems • Explains how the poets have used some features of language, structure and form, using some relevant technical terms • Comments on how some of the techniques used in the poems affect the reader • Shows a clear understanding of the ideas, themes, attitudes and/or context of the poems

Have a go at marking this sample answer extract

Q1 Use the mark scheme to put the sample answer extract below into a grade band, then explain why you've chosen that band.

> Compare how individual experiences are presented in 'War Photographer' and one other poem from 'Power and Conflict'.

> The photographer in 'War Photographer' and the speaker in 'London' are both essentially alone. The speaker in 'London' has a personal experience as he walks around on his own and is angry about the suffering he sees. The third-person narrator in 'War Photographer' also presents the photographer as alone — "he is finally alone". This shows that the process of developing his photos is an individual experience. The reader feels sorry for the speaker in 'London' because he seems angry and has no one to share this with. The photographer in 'War Photographer' seems happy to be alone.

Grade band: .... **Explanation:** ....

....

....

Marking Sample Answers

Take a look at these extracts from answers to the question on page 59

Q2 For each extract, state which grade band you think it should be in, then give a short explanation for your choice. Make sure you refer back to the mark scheme on p.59.

---

a) The individuals in both poems hold views that aren't shared by the rest of society. In 'London', the second stanza develops with the forceful repetition of "In every", which leads to the contrasting final line of "The mind-forged manacles I hear." The emphasis therefore falls on "I hear", highlighting the speaker's individuality and implying that he feels he is the only one aware of these problems. There is a similar separation between the photographer in 'War Photographer' and the newspaper readers, who are apathetic in the face of the suffering that makes the photographer's hands "tremble". This is shown when their eyes "prick / with tears between the bath and pre-lunch beers" after seeing the photographs — the internal rhyme connects "tears" and "beers", but the placement of "beers", with its associations of relaxation and leisure, at the end of the line suggests that they quickly replace any "tears" for the victims of war. In both poems, the individuals appear to want the reader to share in their concerns — the photographer wants people to "care", whilst the speaker in 'London' hopes the reader will share in his desire for social reform.

Grade band: .... Explanation: ....

....

....

....

---

b) 'War Photographer' and 'London' both use examples of individual experiences of suffering to represent suffering on a wider scale. In 'London', the speaker hears the "cry" of an individual sweeper and the "sigh" of an individual soldier. Both of them seem isolated and have no one to help them. The lines that describe these individuals in the third stanza rhyme, which connects the individuals and hints that they were perhaps used by Blake to represent all those who are suffering in the city. Similarly, the photographer in 'War Photographer' remembers observing the dead man who is described as a "half-formed ghost", implying he was on the verge of death. He is just one of a large number of victims of war the photographer has witnessed and documented the stories of through his photographs. The individual suffering presented in 'War Photographer' and 'London' therefore represents wider suffering in the two contexts, but the poets perhaps choose to focus on individual instances of suffering as these could be more emotive for the reader.

Grade band: .... Explanation: ....

....

....

....

Marking Sample Answers

Now try marking this whole answer

Q3 Read the sample answer below, then on p.62 state which grade band you think it should be in and explain why.

> Compare how the reality of war is presented in 'Exposure' and one other poem from 'Power and Conflict'.

If it helps you, label examples of where the answer meets the mark scheme criteria.

Despite 'Exposure' and 'The Charge of the Light Brigade' being written about different conflicts, they both offer an informed insight into the reality of war. 'Exposure' portrays the overwhelming monotony experienced by the soldiers in World War One, who have little company other than each other and the fierce weather conditions. In contrast, the narrator of 'The Charge of the Light Brigade' offers what is almost a eulogy to commemorate the bravery of some of the soldiers who died in the Battle of Balaclava during the Crimean War. Despite their differences, both poets offer a picture of the reality of war that is vicious and unforgiving through aspects of sound, personification, imagery and form.

Both poems use sound to present the horrors of war. In 'Exposure', the alliteration in "flowing flakes that flock, pause, and renew" shows the relentlessness of nature, with the repeated sounds mirroring the onslaught of snow. The caesurae around "pause" could suggest that the soldiers experience temporary respite from the fierce weather — the "pause" perhaps reflecting a moment of hope. However, this quickly dissipates when the snow begins to "renew". Similarly in 'The Charge of the Light Brigade', the sibilance in "Storm'd at with shot and shell" mimics the sound of bullets whizzing towards and around the Light Brigade. This use of sound makes the reader imagine they are in the heat of battle alongside the Light Brigade, heightening the poem's realism.

Each poet uses personification to magnify the threat of death facing the soldiers. In 'Exposure', the "merciless east winds that knive" the soldiers present nature as a fierce killer that wants to harm them. There is a sense of irony to this personification, as the soldiers can't fight back against the wind like they would with an actual enemy. By placing this image on the opening line, a reader could assume that Owen chose to frame the poem with an overriding sense of hopelessness in the face of real danger. Similarly, in 'The Charge of the Light Brigade', the cavalry ride "Into the mouth of Hell". This disturbing image uses language relating to the body to personify "Hell" as a giant figure about to swallow the soldiers. This also reflects the very real suffering in the battle, as "Hell" invokes images of an inferno filled with pain and agonised screams.

The poems' presentations of religion offer contrasting perspectives on hope during the reality of war. The half-line "For love of God seems dying" in 'Exposure' shows that even the sense of hope the soldiers may have had through their faith is withering to the point where all hope is gone. Owen's wording of this line allows for two meanings: firstly, that the soldiers feel that God's love for them is dying, or secondly, that their love for God is dying and they are gradually abandoning their Christian beliefs because of the war. In contrast, religion is used in 'The Charge of the Light Brigade' to bring an aspect of hope to the soldiers' fateful charge. The phrase "All in the valley of Death" is a biblical allusion to Psalm 23, which speaks of God being present with individuals, even when they are faced with evil. This might offer the reader a sense of hope, as it suggests that even after dying in battle, the soldiers would gain eternal life in Heaven.

This answer continues on p.62. ⟶

Marking Sample Answers

Different perspectives in each poem present a contrasting view of the reality of war. The first-person plural narration in 'Exposure', such as in "Our brains ache", gives the conflict a greater sense of realism, as the soldiers' experience of war is presented first-hand. As a serving soldier, Owen was a strong critic of World War One and the cynical aspect of his poetry condemned the more enthusiastic approach to war in traditional war poetry. Through his brutally honest depiction of war and suffering in his poetry, Owen might have hoped to create a sense of protest to war back home. Conversely, the use of a third-person narrator in 'The Charge of the Light Brigade' allows the Light Brigade to be presented as heroes, perhaps ignoring the reality of suffering in war as a consequence. The verbs "Plunged", "Shatter'd" and "Storm'd" use strong, plosive sounds to reflect the power of the charge, showing that despite being vastly outnumbered and outgunned, the soldiers still fought bravely. In contrast to 'Exposure', the graphic reality of suffering is not explicitly presented in 'The Charge of the Light Brigade' giving the soldiers a saint-like quality, as if the narrator did not wish to distract from the soldiers' sacrifice with gruesome images of suffering.

Both poems use form to reinforce how the reality of war is presented. The regular rhyme scheme (ABBAC) in 'Exposure' reflects the monotony the soldiers feel in the trenches. Furthermore, the rhymes are often jagged half-rhymes, for example "stormy" and "army", reflecting how the soldiers' experience of war was not a comfortable one. In a different way, in 'The Charge of the Light Brigade', the intensity of the charge is reinforced through the poem's driving, fast-paced rhythm, partially created by the frequent repetition of phrases at the beginning of stanzas. By using this surging rhythm, Tennyson emphasises the bravery of the soldiers, especially in charging on regardless even though "Some one had blunder'd" in giving them the order. Crucially however, despite the narrator's emphasis on the soldier's bravery, the poem doesn't avoid the reality of the deadliness of war. The poem is punctuated by unrhymed lines, breaking the momentum and perhaps symbolising soldiers being cut down by enemy fire.

Despite writing about different wars in different centuries, Owen and Tennyson both present the vicious and unforgiving reality of war. Both use sound and rhythm to mimic the aspects of war, personification to emphasise the dangers faced by the soldiers and form to present different perspectives of this harsh reality. The scathingly bleak tone in 'Exposure' and the huge loss of life in 'The Charge of the Light Brigade' are used to question the point of war. Where they differ most prominently, however, is that while the religious imagery in 'The Charge of the Light Brigade' implies a subdued sense of hope that the fallen soldiers may be granted eternal life, the soldiers' dying "love of God" in 'Exposure' reflects the utter hopelessness that characterises the reality of war.

Grade band: .... **Explanation:** ....

....

....

....

....

I used to want to sample chocolates — now I sample answers...

Now you're familiar with the mark scheme, you should know exactly what an examiner wants to see. There's a little surprise in store for you on p.64 to help you put everything you've learnt from this section into practice...

Writing Well

Even if your essay contains the best ideas in the world, your writing style needs to be top-notch too in order to impress the examiner. Use the correct technical terms and sophisticated language, write concisely and accurately, and structure your sentences and paragraphs clearly. You also need to use correct spelling, punctuation and grammar throughout — don't let any silly mistakes distract the examiner from your points. Leaving a few minutes to check your writing should help you avoid this.

Q1 Read the following extract from a sample answer.
Cross out and correct all of the spelling and punctuation mistakes.

> 'The Charge of the Light Brigade' and 'Bayonet Charge' both empasise the sounds of battle. Tenyson repeats the onamatopoeic verb "thunder'd" to mimic the noise of the cannons that the soldiers faced Similarly, in 'bayonet charge', the metaphor "blue crackling air" vividly depicks the noise of gunfire by using forceful consonents such as 'b' and 'k'.

Q2 Rewrite the following sample answer using more sophisticated language and technical terms.

> When the storm happens in 'Storm on the Island', phrases often continue from one line to the next. This is different to the way they finish at the end of each line at the start of the poem, and makes you think that the safe feeling the islanders had has gone away.

....

....

....

....

Q3 Rewrite the following sample answer so that it is appropriate for the exam.

> The narrator of 'War Photographer' talks about the photographer as he develops his photos. They call the bits of film "spools of suffering set out in ordered rows". I reckon this is meant to link to the rows of graves of soldiers. It also shows how the photographer is taking the chaos of the war and making it into something he can organise.

....

....

....

....

....

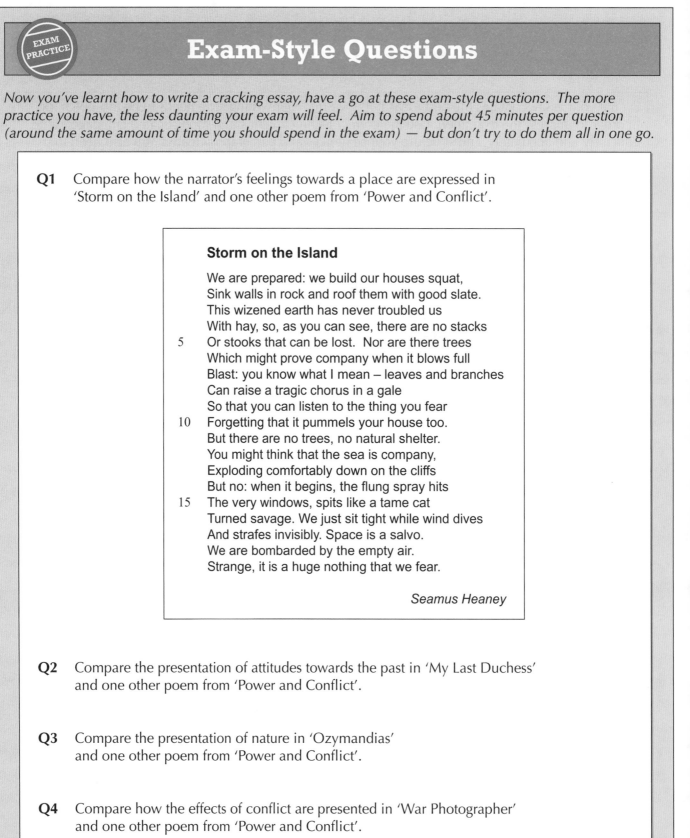

Exam-Style Questions

Now you've learnt how to write a cracking essay, have a go at these exam-style questions. The more practice you have, the less daunting your exam will feel. Aim to spend about 45 minutes per question (around the same amount of time you should spend in the exam) — but don't try to do them all in one go.

Q1 Compare how the narrator's feelings towards a place are expressed in 'Storm on the Island' and one other poem from 'Power and Conflict'.

Storm on the Island

We are prepared: we build our houses squat,
Sink walls in rock and roof them with good slate.
This wizened earth has never troubled us
With hay, so, as you can see, there are no stacks
5 Or stooks that can be lost. Nor are there trees
Which might prove company when it blows full
Blast: you know what I mean – leaves and branches
Can raise a tragic chorus in a gale
So that you can listen to the thing you fear
10 Forgetting that it pummels your house too.
But there are no trees, no natural shelter.
You might think that the sea is company,
Exploding comfortably down on the cliffs
But no: when it begins, the flung spray hits
15 The very windows, spits like a tame cat
Turned savage. We just sit tight while wind dives
And strafes invisibly. Space is a salvo.
We are bombarded by the empty air.
Strange, it is a huge nothing that we fear.

Seamus Heaney

Q2 Compare the presentation of attitudes towards the past in 'My Last Duchess' and one other poem from 'Power and Conflict'.

Q3 Compare the presentation of nature in 'Ozymandias' and one other poem from 'Power and Conflict'.

Q4 Compare how the effects of conflict are presented in 'War Photographer' and one other poem from 'Power and Conflict'.

Q5 Compare the ways poets explore the theme of identity in 'The Emigrée' and one other poem from 'Power and Conflict'.

Answers

These poems have multiple interpretations and there are various quotes that you could use to illustrate your points. There can be lots of right answers when writing about poetry, so just make sure your interpretations are well-explained and supported by evidence. These answers are suggestions for what you could have written.

Section One — The Poems

Pages 2-3: Ozymandias

1. It tells you that the statue is broken and has started to become buried by the desert sand.
2. The word "mock'd" creates humour because while it might simply mean that the sculptor replicated Ozymandias's likeness, it could also be a pun that suggests the sculptor made fun of Ozymandias through the statue.
3. Arrogance. Quote: "Look on my works, ye Mighty, and despair!" Explanation: Ozymandias challenges other rulers and arrogantly assumes that they will "despair" when they see his works.
    Loss of power. Quote: "Two vast and trunkless legs of stone / Stand in the desert."
    Explanation: The remains of the "vast" statue imply it was once a symbol of huge power, but now all that is left of that is a ruin.
4. Shelley uses irony to undermine Ozymandias's arrogance. After the ruler's boasting, the traveller says that "Nothing" of his great civilisation remains apart from the "decay / Of that colossal wreck" — referencing Ozymandias's statue. This use of irony also emphasises the temporary nature of human power in general.
5. The poem suggests that art can be a symbol of power as Ozymandias uses the statue as a way to demonstrate his own power. However, the statue's ruin suggests that the power of art is only temporary, especially when compared to the vast, eternal power of both time and nature.
6. Quote: "boundless and bare / The lone and level sands stretch far away."
    Explanation: Shelley places this image of nature's supremacy at the end of the poem and shows that nature has reclaimed the land that once belonged to the ruler. In this way, Shelley explores 'Romantic' beliefs about the power of nature and implies that nature is in fact more powerful than humanity.
7. This viewpoint undermines Ozymandias's power because it suggests that the narrator only learns about him and the statue through the traveller. This further emphasises the insignificance of Ozymandias's rule and adds irony to his arrogant inscription because the narrator is unable to look upon Ozymandias's "works" as the ruler commands.
Task: You might have included the following points:
*   Art is presented as a symbol of power in both poems. The "vast" statue in 'Ozymandias' and the Duke's art collection in 'My Last Duchess' represent their wealth and status. They also illustrate the individuals' arrogance, because they are both keen for others to "Look on" and "Notice" their artwork.
*   Both poems link specific works of art to human power. While Ozymandias's statue was a symbol of his power, its reduction to a "wreck" shows that his power has been lost. In contrast, after showing his visitor the painting of his last Duchess (a sign of his lasting power over her), the Duke highlights an imposing statue of Neptune "Taming a sea-horse", perhaps warning the visitor that he will "tame" his next Duchess if necessary.

Pages 4-5: London

1. The speaker wanders through the streets of London and describes the suffering that he witnesses.
2. The rhyme scheme in the poem is ABAB. This strict form reflects the monotonous misery and restrictiveness of the city, and implies that this will never change.
3. The use of emotive language highlights the narrator's anger at the situation in the city. Phrases such as "Blasts the new-born infant's tear" are shocking and saddening as they suggest a brutal corruption of innocence from the moment of birth, showing how deadly and uncontrollable the depravity in the city is.
4. Hopelessness. Quote: "blights with plagues the marriage hearse."
    Explanation: This suggests that there is no hope to be found, as even something as happy as marriage has become associated with illness and death.
    Individual experiences. Quote: "I wander through each chartered street"

Explanation: The use of a first-person narrator shows that the poem is a personal account of the narrator's walk around the city.
5. It suggests the narrator believes that people in power are to blame for the suffering in London. Describing the soldier as "hapless" implies that he is unable to do anything, and the image of his "blood" running down the "palace walls" suggests that the powerful people inside have his blood on their hands.
6. Repetition: It reinforces the horror of the situation, especially the repetition of "every" which highlights the massive number of people that are affected.
    Contrast: Oxymorons such as "marriage hearse" suggest there is no hope for the people and their suffering will continue.
7. It makes the poem seem more personal and real because the first-person narration gives authenticity to the account. This makes it easier for the reader to sympathise with the narrator, which in turn makes their use of rhetoric even more persuasive.
Task: You might have included the following points:
*   The presentation of the city in 'The Emigrée' is arguably less emotive than the presentation of place in 'London', in which the city seems more real. In 'London', the narrator's negative descriptions of misery in the city such as "In every cry of every man" are emotive — the repetition of "every" emphasises the widespread suffering. However, in 'The Emigrée', the fact that the speaker gives a nostalgic, positive presentation of a city that is potentially "at war" makes her portrayal seem idealistic, and therefore less emotive.
*   In 'London', the narrator is physically present in the city, allowing him to present the harsh reality first-hand. The use of the present tense also makes it seem more immediate, as though the narrator needs to share his concerns straight away while he is still walking. Conversely, in 'The Emigrée', the narrator's increased distance allows for a more idealised presentation of place. This distance is both geographical and temporal because she hasn't lived in the country since she was a child. She describes her memory of the country as "sunlight-clear", implying that she views it nostalgically. This reliance on memory also makes the presentation of place seem less realistic than in 'London'.

Pages 6-7: The Prelude: Stealing the Boat

1. a) "like one who rows, / Proud of his skill"
   b) "With trembling oars I turned"
2. The beginning of the extract has a positive and idealised tone, which Wordsworth creates by emphasising the narrator's confidence and presenting nature as tranquil and calming.
3. Line: 21 — "When, from behind that craggy steep till then"
    Explanation: The extract changes as the mountain begins to appear and the narrator's confidence turns to insecurity. The tranquil images of nature are replaced by the frightening form of the "black and huge" mountain.
4. Personification. Quote: "Strode after me."
    Explanation: The personification of the mountain as something that can move shows just how threatened the narrator felt by it.
    Oxymoron. Quote: "troubled pleasure"
    Explanation: This shows the narrator's guilt at stealing the boat and foreshadows the trouble it will cause later in the poem.
    Simile. Quote: "my boat / Went heaving through the water like a swan;"
    Explanation: This simile reflects his connection with nature and how he feels confident in his natural surroundings.
5. Lack of rhyme: The lack of rhyme gives the poem a serious quality, reflecting the "grave / And serious mood" that the speaker is left in after his encounter.
    Rhythm: The regular rhythm of the poem gives it a natural quality as though the narrator is using everyday speech, which makes the dramatic experience sound more credible but also compelling.
6. Quote: "Small circles glittering idly in the moon"
    Explanation: As nature changes in the poem, so does the narrator's emotional state. When there are "glittering" circles of water, the narrator exhibits a happy confidence, but when these disappear and are replaced by the "black and huge" mountain, the 'Romantic' power of nature troubles rather than inspires the narrator and he becomes swamped by fear.
Task: You might have included the following points:
*   In 'Ozymandias', human arrogance is presented through the inscription where Ozymandias challenges other rulers to look on his "works" and "despair!" The permanent nature of the inscription highlights his arrogance because it literally sets it in

66

Answers

stone. The confidence of the narrator in 'The Prelude' arguably borders on arrogance when he compares himself to one who rows with "an unswerving line". However, this arrogance is less hyperbolic than the arrogance in 'Ozymandias', and the narrator's boasts do not have the same threatening tone.
• In both poems, human arrogance is shown to be overpowered by the power of nature. In 'Ozymandias', the statue that symbolises Ozymandias's power becomes buried by the powerful desert sands, and in 'The Prelude', the narrator's confidence is shattered by his encounter with the mountain to the point where all he can think about are the "huge and mighty forms" of nature.

Pages 8-9: My Last Duchess

1. a) The Duke is controlling and revels in this power.
   b) People are intimidated by the Duke and his temper, and do not dare to request things of him.
   c) The Duke had his wife murdered.
2. There is a strict use of rhyming couplets throughout the poem, which reflects the Duke's need for absolute control.
3. Displaying a portrait of the Duchess gives the Duke a sense of power and control over her that he was unable to achieve when she was alive. The portrait may also be intended to serve as a warning to others not to cross the Duke.
4. Jealousy. Quote: "She had / A heart – how shall I say? – too soon made glad,"
   Explanation: This implies that the Duke became jealous at how easy it was for other people to make the Duchess happy too.
   Pride. Quote: "Notice Neptune, though, / Taming a sea-horse, thought a rarity,"
   Explanation: Showing off his possessions to the visitor emphasises the Duke's pride in them and, by extension, himself.
5. Enjambment: The enjambment (e.g. lines 13-24) suggests the Duke gets carried away when criticising the Duchess.
   Rhetorical questions: Not allowing the visitor to respond to questions shows the Duke's control as well as his egotism.
6. The Duke's pride, jealousy and arrogance immediately raise questions about whether he may exaggerate or twist the narrative to suit himself. His false modesty when he refers to "skill / In speech – (which I have not)" makes the reader doubt his reliability when describing the Duchess and her alleged faults.
Task: You might have included the following points:
   • The visitor is used as a plot device to provide the context of the Duke arranging to marry his next Duchess. The Duke has clearly moved on from his last Duchess and is quite brazen when talking to the visitor about her.
   • The visitor is used to highlight the Duke's self-obsessed personality. For example, the Duke turns what should be a normal conversation into a monologue, which might suggest that this is the Duke's idea of a conversation.
   • The visitor has neither a voice nor any choice when with the Duke, as he is forcefully told to "sit and look". Likewise in line 53, the Duke almost refuses to let the visitor move by himself, and asserts that they'll "go / Together". This makes the tone of the poem more sinister, by emphasising the Duke's power.

Pages 10-11: The Charge of the Light Brigade

1. The Light Brigade are charging into the valley on horseback. The phrase "valley of Death" creates an ominous feeling and suggests the soldiers won't come back alive.
2. It presents them as a single group with a common goal.
3. Repetition. Quote: "Cannon to right of them, / Cannon to left of them, / Cannon in front of them"
   Explanation: It suggests the soldiers are being ensnared by death. The reader shares in the soldiers' sense of dread as more cannons are revealed.
   Onomatopoeia. Quote: "Shatter'd"
   Explanation: Onomatopoeic sound reflects the chaos, discomfort and destruction of battle.
4. Tennyson's use of a third-person narrator gives the poem a grand scale as it allows the entire battle to be described by an outside observer. This also gives it a story-like quality which implies the soldiers will be immortalised for their bravery.
5. a) The sibilance of "shot and shell" mimics the sound of ammunition whizzing past the soldiers, and "Storm'd" suggests that it is all around them and they cannot escape it.
   b) By personifying "Death" and "Hell" as giant beings that the

soldiers can ride into the mouths of, Tennyson makes the threat of death more real, to the point of being unavoidable.
6. Tennyson romanticises the charge as being heroic. For example, the line "O the wild charge they made!" makes the charge sound exciting and filled with "glory". However, this is contrasted with lines such as "Some one had blunder'd:", which undermine the glory of their sacrifice by hinting that it was unnecessary.
Task: You might have included the following points:
   • In 'The Charge of the Light Brigade', violent verbs such as "Shatter'd and sunder'd" illustrate the horrors of war and reflect the toll of the battle on the soldiers. However, this effect is arguably lessened by figurative imagery such as "the jaws of Death" which distances the reader from the graphic images and pain of war. On the other hand, the violence in 'Remains' is created through graphic imagery described with colloquial language. The narrator's description of the looter as "sort of inside out" shows that the horrors of war seem normal to him, whereas most people would be horrified by them. However, these casual, grotesque descriptions also sound childlike, suggesting that he cannot fully comprehend his experiences.
   • In 'The Charge of the Light Brigade', the repetition of lines such as "Rode the six hundred" emphasises the extensiveness of the violence, while sibilance mimics the sound of gunfire, heightening the viciousness of the conflict. In 'Remains', the use of a first-person narrator makes the violence seem more personal, inviting the reader to sympathise with him as an individual.

Pages 12-13: Exposure

1. Nature is presented as incredibly powerful — despite the war, it is the soldiers' most dangerous enemy. The weather is bleak and relentlessly torments the men in the poem.
2. The regular ABBAC rhyme scheme of the poem creates a monotonous tone that reflects the experience of the soldiers. Owen's use of half-rhymes and half lines also creates an uneasy tone that suggests a level of incompleteness in the soldiers' lives.
3. a) Technique: Personification
   Effect: The personification of the snowflakes makes them appear menacing and malicious, as though they are actively seeking out the soldiers to harm them.
   b) Technique: Metaphor
   Effect: The image hints that the men are emotionally cold, as well as alluding to the effects of the freezing weather.
4. The collective voice shows that the horrific suffering is shared by all the soldiers, and gives the poem an eerie mood as though all the soldiers are speaking in unison.
5. Rhetorical questions such as "What are we doing here?" imply that the soldiers question the point of their sacrifice. However, at the end of the poem they "turn back to their dying" because they believe otherwise "kind fires" won't burn or the sun won't "smile true" on children. This suggests that they cling on to the belief that their deaths have purpose.
Task: You might have included the following points:
   • Both poets use bleak imagery throughout their poems to convey hopelessness. In 'London', the image of a "marriage hearse" suggests even happy occasions are tainted and offer no hope. Similarly, in 'Exposure', bleakness is created through the air being "black with snow". This image subverts the traditional associations of white snow being pure and replaces them with blackness, which could represent hopelessness and death.
   • 'Exposure' is arguably more emotive because the men are narrating their own suffering and contemplating their own deaths. The fact that Owen draws upon his own time in the World War One trenches further heightens the emotion. In 'London', despite the emotive images, there is a disconnect between the speaker and the suffering. Blake's occupation as a poet and artist does not add the same emotion to the poem as Owen's experiences do.

Pages 14-15: Storm on the Island

1. a) "We just sit tight while wind dives"
   b) "Nor are there trees / Which might prove company"
2. The island setting emphasises the isolation of the community. This makes it appear more vulnerable to the storm and increases the feeling of helplessness.
3. The negatives emphasise the barrenness of the island, but they also give the sense that the speaker is trying to calm his fears, e.g. by calling the storm a "nothing".

Answers

4.   Security. Quote: "We are prepared:"
     Explanation: This strong declaration that the people are ready for the storm suggests that they feel safe and secure.
     Fear. Quote: "it is a huge nothing that we fear."
     Explanation: The narrator confesses that they fear the invisible storm. The abstract aspect of the storm contrasts with the sturdiness of the islanders' homes.

5.   Direct address: This gives the poem a conversational tone, involving the reader in the narrator's feeling of fear.
     Sibilance: Sibilant sounds, e.g. in "strafes invisibly. Space is a salvo.", mimic the hissing and spitting of the sea.

6.   While nature can appear "tame", safe and familiar like a cat, there is the potential for it to become dangerous, threatening and unpredictable — as it does in the storm.

7.   The oxymoron "Exploding comfortably" reflects the unusual tonal combination of fear and safety in the poem. On the one hand, the islanders are adapted to and comfortable with the force of nature on their island. However, they are also scared of the approaching storm, and "Exploding" highlights the potential for it to be dangerous.

Task: You might have included the following points:
     • The poem might seem more frightening if 'I' was used instead of "we" because the latter suggests a strength via community, whereas 'I' would have presented the narrator as isolated and therefore even more helpless against the storm.
     • The islanders have to "just sit tight" which suggests they helplessly await their fate at the mercy of the storm. The closing image of the "huge nothing" that's against them adds to this sense that they are now helpless against nature's power.

Pages 16-17: Bayonet Charge

1.   It places the reader in the middle of the action with no explanation, establishing an uncertain tone which highlights the soldier's confusion.

2.   Fear. Quote: "his sweat heavy"
     Explanation: The soldier feels literally weighed down by the sweat caused by his fear.
     Confusion. Quote: "In bewilderment then he almost stopped –"
     Explanation: The soldier's confusion is so overwhelming that he almost stops — the reader becomes concerned for his safety.

3.   Example: "Bullets smacking the belly out of the air"
     Effect: The sound of the bullets figuratively "smacking" the wind out of the air helps the reader to imagine their force.

4.   The soldier appears to have a confused state of mind at first, but in the second stanza he pauses and reflects on his own existence. In the final stanza, however, the soldier drops his principles and terror overwhelms his thoughts.

5.   It suggests that the soldier is only a small part of a cold, soulless universe. The idea of "clockwork" links to mechanisms and order, which implies that the soldier has no control over his own fate — he is simply a cog in a much larger machine.

6.   By placing the turning point in the middle of line 15, Hughes creates a more sudden shift in focus, which surprises the reader more than if the shift came at the start of a new stanza.

7.   The soldier's desperation to drop "King, honour [...] etcetera" shows how unimportant patriotism has become compared to survival. The poem suggests that when the horror of war becomes too overwhelming for soldiers, it is fear and terror that pushes them on rather than any sense of patriotism, which seems to be presented as an ideal that is difficult to uphold in reality.

Task: You might have included the following points:
     • Figurative language including the simile "He lugged a rifle numb as a smashed arm" shows the physical and mental strain on soldiers, and may foreshadow injury to the soldier. This draws sympathy from the reader for the soldier who is clearly suffering.
     • Hughes's violent descriptions of nature effectively reflect the devastation of war. The agony of the hare that "crawled in a threshing circle" could be a metaphor for the soldier, whose innocence has been destroyed by the devastating chaos of war.

Pages 18-19: Remains

1.   He doesn't know whether the looter was armed or not and therefore worries that killing him was wrong.

2.   The poem becomes more personal. What once seemed like a casual anecdote has now turned into a painful confession of a man who can't escape the guilt of his actions.

3.   Repetition. Quote: "his bloody life in my bloody hands."
     Effect: Repetition of "bloody" makes the narrator sound horrified and angry, which could concern or even intimidate the reader.
     Colloquial language. Quote: "One of my mates goes by"
     Effect: This creates a chatty tone, making the death of the looter seem trivial. This triviality shocks the reader.

4.   The short words "Sleep" and "Dream" have plosive sounds in them, i.e. 'p' and 'd', which could resemble gunshots. The sounds are emphasised as the caesurae separate them from the rest of the lines, giving them more force.

5. a) Quote: "tosses his guts back into his body."
       Explanation: The matter-of-fact language suggests killing was a normal thing for the soldiers.
   b) Quote: "the drink and the drugs won't flush him out"
       Explanation: The guilt is so overpowering that the soldier tries unsuccessfully to numb it with alcohol and drugs.

6.   The metaphor shows that the memory of the killing is strongly planted in his mind and it won't go away. Using military imagery also suggests that the soldier is constantly reliving the event — perhaps a sign that he has post-traumatic stress disorder (PTSD).

Task: You might have included the following points:
     • Both poets present psychological turmoil as a result of conflict. In 'Remains', the repetition of the phrase "probably armed, possibly not" shows the soldier's doubt and hints at ongoing psychological conflict. Similarly, in 'Exposure', the opening phrase "Our brains ache" focuses the poem on psychological pain, and the collective possessive determiner "Our" suggests conflict is a shared psychological experience. The assertion that their brains are aching could also refer to shell shock, as it suggests they are unable to comprehend the situation they're in.
     • Form is used to emphasise the psychological effects of conflict in each poem. In 'Exposure', Owen adopts a regular rhyme scheme (ABBAC) which, combined with the repeated half-line "But nothing happens.", emphasises the tediousness of life in the trenches and reinforces the psychological drain on the soldiers. In 'Remains', the caesurae and enjambment in lines 20-21 reinforce the notion that the soldier has been psychologically damaged by this event. Even when he's home, the memory "bursts" into his head — it haunts him and is inescapable.

Pages 20-21: Poppies

1.   The speaker has a loved one who is involved in war in some way. She is affectionately remembering this person.

2.   The enjambment suggests the mother gets lost in recounting the memories of her son. The caesurae show that she's trying to maintain emotional control — it's possible that she keeps having to pause to hold back tears.

3.   Recounting these memories, such as playing "at / being Eskimos", shows how close they were, making her loss seem even greater. However, it could also show that she can't let go of her son and clings to his innocence rather than reminding herself that he's left.

4. a) Doves symbolise peace, which could suggest that the son is at peace — in the sense that he may have died.
   b) Pear trees are often seen as symbols for long life, so the fact the dove has left the tree could mean his life was cut short.

5.   After her son has left, the mother's narration and memories feature a strong use of touch and sound. She recalls touching a lot of things associated with him, e.g. his uniform, which emphasises how much she misses him. Hearing also heightens this sense of loss — she longs to hear his "voice catching on the wind." This perhaps suggests she is trying to find a way to bring him back.

6.   Fear. Quote: "I was brave"
     Explanation: Her short, simple language suggests that she struggled to keep her composure and not show her fear.
     Freedom. Quote: "the world overflowing / like a treasure chest."
     Explanation: This positive simile suggests that the freedom in leaving home was exciting for the son.

Task: You might have included the following points:
     • Both poems feature positive memories which heighten each narrator's sense of loss. In 'The Emigrée', the speaker has such vivid memories of her former city that it's been personified — "My city takes me dancing". This personification, as well as the phrase "I comb its hair", makes the loss seem even more tragic because it shows just how much the speaker wants to be with the former city. Similarly, in 'Poppies', the mother's memories of

Answers

her son's childhood, such as when they would "play at / being Eskimos", emphasises her sense of loss by informing the reader of their love for each other. Ultimately, both speakers cling onto what they have lost, having only their memories to comfort them.
• While the use of memories in both poems heightens each speaker's sense of loss, the mother's sense of loss in 'Poppies' is perhaps presented more successfully. The speaker of 'The Emigrée' is still able to engage with the city as it is present in some way to her, whereas the closest the mother gets to her son in 'Poppies' is in touching the "war memorial".

Pages 22-23: War Photographer

1. It refers to a photo that begins to develop in the darkroom — the photo depicts a man who died in the war zone.
2. Regular rhyme scheme: This reflects the "ordered rows" of the photos and shows that the photographer is methodical with his work, but also that he keeps a tight rein on his emotions.
    Enjambment: This mirrors the gradual revealing of the photos as they develop.
3. Religious imagery. Quote: "All flesh is grass."
    Effect: This Biblical quote about the temporary nature of human life makes the photographer sound like a priest at a funeral.
    Emotive language. Quote: "running children in a nightmare heat"
    Effect: The thought of helpless, panicked children in pain and in a "nightmare" pulls at the reader's heartstrings and makes them question the point of war.
4. It's quiet and calm, which provides a contrast with the war zone the photographer was in. The darkness also hints at the horrific content of the photographs that he's developing.
5. The word "half-formed" could mean that the stranger's body had been mutilated, as it suggests his body wasn't fully intact. "ghost" could represent him passing from life to death.
6. Example: "Belfast. Beirut. Phnom Penh."
    Explanation: The succession of plosive sounds here ('b', 'p' and 't') are used to reflect the sound of gunfire, as they are forceful and quick sounds.
7. The word "impassively" could suggest that the photographer's emotions have been numbed by his job. Alternatively, it could suggest that his job has left him feeling detached from his country — the photographer cares about the victims he takes pictures of, but his fellow countrymen "do not care".
Task: You might have included the following points:
    • The soldier and the photographer both have a duty: one to serve their country and one to document the war, bringing awareness to the conflict and its victims. The photographer's understanding of his duty is presented in the phrase "He has a job to do." The short, monosyllabic words create a matter-of-fact tone and show that he has put aside his emotions to carry out his duty, as a soldier would.
    • The speaker's tone in the final stanza hints at anger or frustration, suggesting that the speaker believes the public are apathetic about wars. The speaker questions the sympathy shown by citizens whose "eyeballs prick / with tears", with "prick" suggesting that their pain was short-lived and quickly forgotten. The sibilance in "Sunday's supplement" could mirror the speaker's anger towards the public's apathy, as it almost sounds like he is spitting the words out.

Pages 24-25: Tissue

1. The poet creates a thoughtful tone and highlights paper's importance by placing it at the start of the first two sentences.
2. a) Quote: "that lets the light / shine through".
    Explanation: The verb "shine" implies a strong burst of light which can illuminate and bring understanding.
   b) Quote: "pages smoothed and stroked and turned / transparent with attention."
    Explanation: The verbs "smoothed" and "stroked" are gentle and show humans have treated the pages with great care.
3. There is no regular rhythm or rhyme scheme which suggests that the narrator longs to be free of restrictions. The enjambment runs not only from line to line but also across stanzas, allowing the poem to flow smoothly which, in turn, emphasises the theme of freedom without boundaries.
4. Control. Quote: "might fly our lives like paper kites"
    Explanation: This simile shows that people are controlled by things — money in this case.

Fragility. Quote: "a structure / never meant to last"
Explanation: Humans are fragile, like paper, and they will eventually die.
5. Dharker might have chosen 'Tissue' as it confirms the poem's connection between human tissue and tissue paper — human lives and paper are both powerful and built up in layers, but ultimately they are fragile.
6. Dharker presents paper, an extended metaphor for life, as being temporary. "Paper thinned by age or touching" suggests that all life eventually comes to an end, and Dharker asserts that "If buildings were paper" people would be more aware of their own temporary nature. However, light is presented as more permanent, for example it can "break / through" and transcend human constructs such as "capitals" and "borderlines".
Task: You might have included the following points:
    • Both poems present human identity as being formed through cultural history. In 'Checking Out Me History', the speaker's repetition of "Dem tell me" shows he is angry at those who have shaped his identity without reference to his cultural history. His discontent reflects the idea that culture is an integral part of human identity. Similarly, in 'Tissue', Dharker suggests heritage is key to forming human identity as paper, a motif for life, is used to record people's "names and histories". The pages being "smoothed and stroked" reflects the importance of family history and heritage in regards to forming human identity.
    • 'Checking Out Me History' uses a first-person narrator who gives a passionate and subjective account of his cultural identity. This voice allows him to give his perspective on his own cultural history without the interference of others, who have previously neglected it. In contrast, the elusive poetic voice in 'Tissue' has a more contemplative tone, allowing the poem to focus more on the ideas presented rather than on the speaker. The direct address "turned into your skin." at the end of the poem makes the reader consider their own identity.

Pages 26-27: The Emigrée

1. The speaker has had to leave a country, but she has a very positive view of the country and remembers it nostalgically.
2. Quote: "time rolls its tanks"
    Effect: The word "tanks" implies that the narrator sees "time" as a militarised enemy that threatens her as it creates a barrier between her and her former city.
    Quote: "I comb its hair and love its shining eyes."
    Effect: The city is personified as a living thing that the speaker can play with and show affection to, suggesting there's such a close connection that she can almost touch it.
3. The enjambment shows that the speaker feels a sense of freedom and her memories are filled with excitement. The end-stopping shows that she feels trapped in her new city.
4. It suggests the speaker's positive memories are permanently ingrained in her. However, "branded" sounds negative, which might suggest that this view of her country was forced onto her.
5. The city is described as having "white streets", which makes it sound almost heavenly, as whiteness is associated with purity. The phrase "the graceful slopes / glow" uses alliteration of the 'g', consonance of the 'l' and assonance of the long 'o' sounds to present an elegant and picturesque description of the city.
6. The repetition of "They" in the last stanza emphasises the difference between the speaker and the people in her new city. The fact that they "mutter" shows that the people don't even speak to her, which characterises her as an isolated figure.
7. They suggest that the speaker doesn't feel safe in her new city — she might have escaped political persecution but "they mutter death" shows she is still in danger. Despite this, she shows optimism in the closing phrase "evidence of sunlight." Her memories of the city perhaps keep her company in the new city.
Task: You might have included the following points:
    • The former city is presented as a potential war zone in line 7: "It may be at war, it may be sick with tyrants". The personifying adjective "sick" presents the city as being plagued with authoritarians, as if they are a disease. The poet reinforces this idea by choosing to use the word "tyrants" rather than, e.g. 'leaders', as the noun 'tyrant' has associations with oppression.
    • The speaker feels threatened in her new "city of walls". This phrase suggests she feels trapped and confined, or that she is being imprisoned there against her will. The phrase "they circle

me" further suggests that she feels threatened, as it reiterates the notion that she is confined. Additionally, the pronoun "they" emphasises the threat she feels, as it presents them as an unknown group, giving their actions a sense of menace.

Pages 28-29: Kamikaze

1. a) The phrase "powerful incantations" makes it seem as though the Kamikaze pilots were under a spell. They were heavily influenced by patriotic propaganda and the glory that came with death.

   b) "one-way" implies that the pilots were not expected to come back alive, while "journey into history" suggests that they would be legendary figures.

2. Lack of pilot's voice: This reflects how he has been cast out by society for not completing his mission. The shame of his failure has cost him his voice.
   Direct speech from daughter: The daughter's factual description of her father's return home is used to present the very personal pain and shame felt by the family.

3. Quote: "a green-blue translucent sea"
   Effect: This image of nature's beauty might have been one of the key reasons why the pilot turned back. This shows how nature can influence humans.
   Quote: "flashing silver as their bellies / swivelled towards the sun"
   Effect: "flashing silver" evokes an image of the pilot's samurai sword, which is ironic because he's abandoning conflict here. The swivelling fish also reflect him changing his mind.

4. The memories reflect a loss of childhood innocence. The pilot's innocent memories, e.g. of building "cairns of pearl-grey pebbles", contrast with his dangerous job. They were perhaps one of the influences that made him change his mind and turn back. The daughter remembers her own loss of innocence when she "learned / to be silent" and shunned her father.

5. a) Quote: "he must have wondered / which had been the better way to die."
   Explanation: The daughter wonders whether her father felt any regret. Perhaps she also empathises with him and regrets treating him as if he was dead.

   b) Quote: "they treated him / as though he no longer existed"
   Explanation: This shows the family felt so much shame upon the pilot's return that they treated him as if he was dead.

6. Although her actions seem cold and cruel, the reader does sympathise with the daughter as she 'lost' her father to a cruel system of patriotism. The fact she "learned / to be silent" suggests her coldness wasn't voluntary.

Task: You might have included the following points:
   • Both the pilot in 'Kamikaze' and the soldiers in 'The Charge of the Light Brigade' are presented as being prepared to die for their country. Where they differ is that the soldiers in 'The Charge of the Light Brigade' actually carried out their duty even when they were given wrong orders. Their obedience is shown in "Theirs not to make reply, / Theirs not to reason why, / Theirs but to do and die". This emphatic repetition is used to stress the subordinate position of the soldiers, who did not question the orders. This contrasts with the pilot in 'Kamikaze', who didn't carry out his mission despite the heavy influences of patriotism.
   • The narrator in 'The Charge of the Light Brigade' seems opposed to the avoidable waste of life, e.g. in the sombre tone of "All that was left of them". However, rather than questioning the worth of patriotism, the narrator focuses on presenting the soldiers as heroes — "When can their glory fade?" In contrast, the speaker in 'Kamikaze' seems to be more directly critical of patriotism, particularly patriotism underpinned by propaganda. The speaker's feeling is reflected through the sombre tone of the final lines where the pilot's metaphorical death is revealed and the destructiveness of patriotism exposed.

Pages 30-31: Checking Out Me History

1. The speaker seems to be angry at "Dem" for only giving him limited information. He speaks with a distinctive accent in non-Standard English.

2. Agard uses non-Standard English spellings, e.g. "dem" and "de", as a sort of rebellion against the British education system, because he is angry that his own cultural history isn't taught. This spelling is also representative of his own cultural background, showing he is proud of his identity.

3. Anger. Quote: "no dem never tell me bout dat"

Explanation: The double negative makes the speaker sound angry about not being taught his own cultural history.
Admiration. Quote: "a healing star"
Explanation: The speaker describes Mary Seacole with a metaphor associated with hope and holiness.
Celebration. Quote: "But now I checking out me own history"
Explanation: The speaker is going to embrace his own history and identity. This contrasts with the angry tone seen at the beginning of the poem.

4. Stanza forms: Agard's use of stanzas with shorter lines for the Caribbean history slows the pace and makes them seem more serious than the British ones.
Sentence structure: The broken sentences used when describing Caribbean history make the speaker's words sound like a chant or a drum beat, which reflects Caribbean culture and almost forces the reader to listen. In comparison, the sentence structure in the British stanzas is more restricted by convention.

5. The figurative use of blindness in "Blind me to me own identity" reflects how the history he's been taught intentionally omits his own cultural history. This blindness also contrasts with the Caribbean figures such as Toussaint L'Ouverture, who is portrayed as having "vision", suggesting he has an awareness of his identity and heritage — something the speaker desires.

Task: You might have included the following points:
   • The narrator in 'London' displays anger towards "Every black'ning church" and "palace walls", suggesting he's angry at the people in power for not doing anything to change the bleak situation he sees. Anger directed at those in power is also seen in 'Checking Out Me History', where the speaker is angry at the British education system ("dem") for not teaching him about his own Caribbean history.
   • In 'London', emotive language such as "the youthful harlot's curse / Blasts the new-born infant's tear" emphasises the narrator's anger at the social problems. For example, the "curse" could be interpreted as a sexually transmitted disease, as they were widespread at the time. The fact that this has been blasted onto the child suggests its innocence has been forcibly corrupted. This contrasts with 'Checking Out Me History' where the speaker's anger is accentuated through the use of comical language to describe British history, such as "de cow who jump over de moon" — this trivialises it compared to his own history.

Page 32: Using Quotes

1. a) "our ghosts"
   b) "fall away on a sigh"
2. a) "a blockade / of yellow bias binding"
   b) "On another occasion"
3. In 'The Prelude', Wordsworth presents the narrator as "Proud of his skill" to show his confidence while rowing the boat, although this confidence could be interpreted as arrogance. Similarly, the Duke in 'My Last Duchess' is proud of his "nine-hundred-years-old name", but his pride also borders on arrogance as he boasts about his family's status.

Page 33: P.E.E.D.

1. a) Missing stage: Example. Addition: She says that she "left it as a child" but that her "memory of it is sunlight-clear".
   b) Missing stage: Explanation. Addition: The word "luxuries" suggests that these patriotic concepts are unnecessary in the heat of battle and become almost a burden to the soldier.
2. Development: In 'Ozymandias', this representation of power through a physical object feels arrogant and vain, whereas in 'Tissue' it is reassuring and empowering for the reader.

Section Two — Themes

Page 34: Power of Humans

1. a) Quote: "How the chimney-sweeper's cry / Every black'ning church appals"
   Explanation: The Church is appalled by social problems such as child labour, rather than using its power to act. "black'ning" hints the Church is corrupt and shows the poet's disapproval of it.
   b) Quote: "Bandage up me eye with me own history"
   Explanation: This metaphor implies that the speaker believes the British education system purposely hid his own history from him.

Answers

2. The dramatic monologue allows the Duke to present himself as dominant, with no other voices being heard. This could mirror how he expects people to see things as he does, e.g. he chose "Never to stoop" to criticise his wife because he felt he shouldn't have needed to remind her of how he expected her to behave.

3. Human constructs of power, e.g. nations, borders and capitals, are presented as fragile in the way that something as gentle as "daylight" can "break / through" them. The image of paper "thinned to be transparent, // turned into your skin." could suggest humans are also fragile.

4. Ozymandias's "cold command" suggests that he was dictatorial and subjected his people to various atrocities — "cold" implies a lack of emotion or empathy. Additionally, "sneer" suggests he had a lack of respect for his people, as if he felt his power made him better than them. The sculptor's decision to reproduce this feature hints that it was a defining feature of the ruler.

Exam Practice:
Your answer should have an introduction, several paragraphs developing different ideas and a conclusion. You may have covered some of the following points:
• The establishment in 'London' and the Duke in 'My Last Duchess' are both presented as misusing their power. Blake's narrator describes how "blood" runs "down palace walls" which shows the establishment is uncaring, as the "walls" separate the rulers inside the palace and the people suffering outside of it. Similarly in Browning's poem, the Duke's assertion that he "gave commands; / Then all smiles stopped" euphemistically implies that he abused his power by having his wife killed. The Duke's authoritarian power contrasts with the establishment not using their power to help the citizens in 'London'.
• Both poems explore a psychological aspect of power. The narrator in 'London' describes the citizens as being trapped in "mind-forged manacles", a metaphor that suggests they are trapped through their own belief that their situation is inescapable. In 'My Last Duchess', the Duke's psychological power over others is shown by him manipulating the 'conversation' and intimidating the visitor with mention of his "nine-hundred-years-old name" — a clear indication of his status. The reader gets the sense that the Duke is aware of and empowered by the psychological aspect of power, whereas the citizens in 'London' do not realise the negative effect of their psychological state.
• The speakers in the poems have contrasting degrees of power. The dramatic monologue form of 'My Last Duchess' reflects the Duke's absolute power as he has complete control over both the poem and his circumstances. The Duke revels in this power and states "if they durst", almost taunting others to challenge him. In contrast, the narrator's power in 'London' is limited. While the dramatic monologue form gives him control of the poem, he is only able to comment on what he sees. This is shown through the repetition of "In every" as it suggests the narrator is frustrated at the bleak situation and his inability to do anything. Blake was an outspoken critic of social inequality, so the speaker's frustration may reflect the poet's own frustration at lacking the power to change society.

Page 35: Power of Nature

1. The poem suggests that the pilot's childhood memories may have been important, but the sheer quantity of beautiful natural imagery, e.g. "green-blue translucent sea", hints that it was nature that made the pilot change his mind.

2. Violent images of war such as "Exploding" and "bombarded" are used to compare the storm to a cannon or a bomber plane, emphasising the danger it poses. This is further exaggerated through plosive sounds including "pummels" and "Blast" which make the storm sound forceful as it hits the island.

3. Humans are presented as being inferior to "boundless" nature, which outlasts not only human life, but also the man-made structures humans have made in their name.

4. In 'Exposure', the personification of nature in phrases such as "iced east winds that knive us" makes it seem dangerous. The mountain in 'The Prelude' is also personified to make it seem threatening, e.g. "Upreared its head". This creates a sense of danger as what was once an inanimate mountain now appears to actively pursue him. This makes the mountain in 'The Prelude' seem like a nightmare, whereas nature in 'Exposure' is presented

as a very real threat and therefore seems more dangerous.

Page 36: Effects of Conflict

1. The soldiers feel as though people back home have forgotten about them, as shown when they say "Shutters and doors, all closed: on us the doors are closed". The caesurae and repetition of "closed" reinforce how separated and shut out they feel. It suggests they believe that people at home have lost interest in the war, which makes their reason for being there less compelling.

2. Both poems present the psychological effects of war through characters who are uncomfortable at home and detached from society. The soldier in 'Remains' is wracked with guilt, as seen in the poem's final image of his "bloody hands". This is similar to the photographer in 'War Photographer', whose hands "tremble" at home, perhaps showing that the conflict he's seen disturbs him.

3. The repetition of "six hundred" constantly reminds the reader of the number of individuals involved. The forceful repetition of "cannon" in the third and fifth stanzas reinforces the fact that the Light Brigade are surrounded and creates an ominous sense that many of the "six hundred" are about to face death.

4. The effects of conflict on families are seen through each family's emotional response. In 'Poppies', the sensory language such as "graze my nose" reflects the mother's grief, as it shows the intimate relationship she had with her son, which has now been lost. This contrasts with the less emotional response of the daughter in 'Kamikaze'. This is shown through *to live as though / he had never returned* which has a repressed tone, suggesting she had to suppress her emotions in relating to her father.

Exam Practice:
Your answer should have an introduction, several paragraphs developing different ideas and a conclusion. You may have covered some of the following points:
• In both 'Bayonet Charge' and 'Exposure', conflict causes a shift in expectations. In 'Bayonet Charge', the soldier believed he was fighting for "King" and "honour", but these expectations are "Dropped like luxuries", showing they are of no use to him and are simply a burden. In 'Exposure', the repetition of "But nothing happens." at the end of four stanzas suggests the soldiers expected more to happen in the war, but instead it's painfully monotonous. The shifts in expectations in both poems contrast with the idealistic view of war displayed in more traditional war poetry, where war was often romanticised or glorified.
• The soldiers in both poems become isolated by conflict. In 'Bayonet Charge', the poet highlights soldier's isolation as he is the only living thing described in the poem, save for a "green hedge" and a "yellow hare" which offer no comfort or assistance in his bewildered state. In contrast, the soldiers in 'Exposure' state that "Shutters and doors, all closed: on us the doors are closed, –" showing that while they have each other's company, it is little comfort because they feel abandoned and isolated by their loved ones. The caesura in this line emphasises their isolation, creating a barrier between the soldiers and those at home. In 'Bayonet Charge' isolation is associated with being in a state of confusion, whereas in 'Exposure' it's associated with resignation.
• Conflict causes the soldiers in both poems to lose hope. In 'Bayonet Charge', the symbolism of fate in "In what cold clockwork of the stars" reflects the soldier's inability to control his own fate and implies that there is no hope for him to change it. In contrast, the soldiers in 'Exposure' feel hopeless against the relentless and inescapable power of nature, as shown in "the merciless east winds that knive" them. This image personifies nature, which creates a sense of irony as the solders can't fight it as they could a human enemy. The hopelessness in both poems draws sympathy from the reader, who senses that in both cases the soldiers' situations are so hopeless that they are doomed to die.

Page 37: Reality of Conflict

1. Tennyson uses sounds to imitate the sounds of the battlefield and immerse the reader in the scene. Plosives, e.g. "Plunged", and onomatopoeia, e.g. "thunder'd", mimic the boom of cannons. Sibilance in "sabre stroke / Shatter'd and sunder'd" sounds violent, as it imitates the sound of a sabre swooshing through the air.

2. As it happens. Poem: 'Bayonet Charge'
Effect: It creates a sense of immediacy which helps the reader to sympathise with the soldier, who is faced with the very real and current threat of danger.

Answers

After the event. Poem: 'Remains'
Effect: Using hindsight allows the poet to explore the long-lasting effect of conflict in everyday life after war.

3. Images such as "Shrivelling many hands, puckering foreheads crisp." present the horrifying image of the soldiers' frozen bodies. Images of bodily horror combine with images of psychological horror such as "our ghosts drag home", presenting the soldiers as caught in a horrifying state of limbo between life and death.

4. Verbs such as "Stumbling" and "dazzled" present the soldier as out of control, as they suggest that he is scared and confused by the gunshots that surround him. The simile "He lugged a rifle numb as a smashed arm" not only describes the physical strain of the conflict on the soldier, but could also predict the injuries he might receive, which characterises him as a victim of war.

Page 38: Loss and Absence

1. The soldiers are described as heroes in "They that had fought so well", reflecting the poem's purpose as a tribute to those from the Light Brigade who died in the Battle of Balaclava during the Crimean War. "All the world wonder'd" suggests that the narrator, as with many in Britain, questioned the loss of life.

2. Quote: "my city comes to me"
Explanation: She personifies the city as something she can engage with to alleviate her feeling of absence. This is reinforced by her combing its hair, as it shows there is an intimate bond between the two.

3. The Duke shows no sense of sadness over the loss of his wife and instead focuses on her perceived negative aspects. His disgust at her alleged flirting is reinforced through the repetition of "spot of joy" — a blush that he judges to be evidence of her guilt. The Duke's emotions disturb the reader, who fears for the woman lined up to be his next wife.

4. The soldiers in 'Exposure' "cringe in holes" which implies that the situation has reduced them to helpless creatures who have no hope of escaping. In 'London', images of suffering such as the "infant's cry of fear" depict society as hellish. However, the narrator suggests that the citizens' mindsets ("mind-forged manacles") reinforce the cycle of suffering, therefore presenting them as hopeless, because they are unwilling to help themselves.

Exam Practice:
Your answer should have an introduction, several paragraphs developing different ideas and a conclusion. You may have covered some of the following points:
• 'Kamikaze' and 'The Emigrée' both present characters who have lost something dear to them. The daughter in 'Kamikaze' feels as though she has lost her father because he has been ostracised by society and she has to *"live as though / he had never returned"*. This direct speech is matter-of-fact, creating a solemn tone that hints at the pain of her 'loss', which in turn draws sympathy from the reader. Similarly, in 'The Emigrée', the opening "There once was a country..." creates an immediate sense of personal loss as it is in the past tense. Through the speaker's melancholy tone in the opening, Rumens frames the whole poem with a sense of loss.
• 'The Emigrée' deals with individual loss, whereas the loss in 'Kamikaze' is collective. The first-person narrative voice in 'The Emigrée' presents the loss of the city as a personal experience — there is no mention of other people who presumably also left the city. The repetition of "they" in the final stanza compounds her individual loss, as those in the new city oppose her. In contrast, in 'Kamikaze' the collective loss experienced by the pilot's children, wife and neighbours is shown through the long sentence that spans two stanzas. This shows that the sense of loss is far-reaching and affects a whole community. A reader might feel that this collective sense of loss is easier to deal with than an individual feeling of loss because it is shared.
• Each poem presents contrasting views of how personal loss is dealt with. The speaker in 'The Emigrée' deals with the loss of her city by engaging with an imagined, personified version of it — she states "I comb its hair and love its shining eyes". The iambic pentameter used in this line gives the rhythm a melodic quality, as if she is singing a lullaby to herself to ease her loss. Conversely, the daughter in 'Kamikaze' *"learned / to be silent"*, with the verb *"learned"* perhaps implying she had to suppress her emotions to deal with loss. The more serious tone in 'Kamikaze' suggests the speaker understands the reality of her loss, but the speaker's

childlike descriptions in 'The Emigrée' hint at a nostalgia that prevents her from engaging with the reality of the loss.

Page 39: Memory

1. Poppies are a symbol to remember the sacrifice of those who died in World War One and subsequent conflicts. This reflects the mother in the poem remembering her son after he leaves.

2. The speaker describes her memories as being "sunlight-clear", which suggests she thinks they are perfectly reliable. However, "The worst news [...] cannot break / my original view" implies they may not be fully reliable, as it suggests her views could be distorted by optimism and nostalgia.

3. The developing photos appear to cause his memories to resurface and the horror of them has a physical effect on him. This suggests that he couldn't process this horror in the war zone, but at home the horrors of war begin to affect him.

4. It causes him to have a negative perception of nature after the event. Nature no longer seems "familiar" or "pleasant" to him as it did at the beginning of the extract. His initial care-free attitude has disappeared and he anxiously struggles to comprehend the "unknown modes of being", reinforcing how the memory of the mountain now troubles his "dreams".

Page 40: Negative Emotions

1. The photographer may feel guilty in the sense that he "earns his living" from documenting other people's suffering. On the other hand, he feels that it's his duty to "do what someone must" and inform the public of the horrors of war.

2. The shift from the first-person plural "we" to the first-person singular "I" suggests the narrator feels personally responsible. This feeling is emphasised through the metaphor in the last line of the poem, which suggests the looter's life and death was in his hands.

3. On a physical level, the soldier isn't in control of his body as he runs "Like a man who has jumped up in the dark". His behaviour in this simile and his listening "for the reason / Of his still running" indicates that his mind has lost control of his body. The mechanical language in the "cold clockwork of the stars" also implies that the soldier is controlled by some greater force.

4. At the beginning of 'The Prelude', the speaker is full of confidence and "Proud of his skill". This is similar to 'Storm on the Island', as the islanders feel "prepared" for the storm. However, the people in both poems are seemingly punished for their hubris — in 'The Prelude' nature is now a "trouble" to the speaker's "dreams" after his encounter with the mountain, and the islanders in 'Storm on the Island' lose their confidence in the face of nature's power, which terrifies them.

Exam Practice:
Your answer should have an introduction, several paragraphs developing different ideas and a conclusion. You may have covered some of the following points:
• 'Poppies' and 'Storm on the Island' both explore the fear of loss. The mother in 'Poppies' seems to fear that her son isn't coming back. After she releases "a song bird from its cage", which could symbolise the son leaving home, the mother sees "a single dove" near the church yard, with the graveyard location meaning she may fear her son has died. The frequent mentions of graves and memorials seems to show how she is consumed by this fear. By comparison, there seems to be nothing the islanders in 'Storm on the Island' fear losing, for example "there are no stacks / Or stooks that can be lost". This is ironic, because it is the island's barrenness and inhospitable nature that means there is nothing to lose. Since the islanders don't fear losing property, the reader begins to wonder about what they actually do fear.
• Each poem uses language of war to instil a sense of fear in the reader. In 'Storm on the Island', the islanders are "bombarded" by the storm. This image compares the storm to a bomber plane that indiscriminately beats down on the islanders, and presents nature as a destructive force to be feared. Similarly, in 'Poppies', Weir repeatedly uses language associated with injury. For example, even everyday items such as "Sellotape®" are "bandaged". This creates an overwhelming sense that her son will be or has been injured or killed, leaving the reader fearful.
• Both poems explore the fear of the unknown. In 'Poppies' the metaphorical language associated with sewing in "stomach busy / making tucks, darts, pleats" shows the physical impact of the mother's nervous worry and anxiety, and suggests that she feels

sick over not knowing the fate of her son. Similarly in 'Storm on the Island', the islanders' fear of the unknown is shown through the oxymoron "it is a huge nothing we fear". This shows that, although the storm is not a solid force, they fear the havoc it might cause. Through this, both poems might be suggesting that the fear of the unknown is worse than the fear of what is known.

Page 41: Identity

1. Quote: "hoping to hear / your playground voice".
   Explanation: Ending the poem with this phrase shows the mother prefers to think of her son as a schoolboy rather than as a soldier.
2. The phrase suggests all humans are made up of the same "living tissue" and are therefore all equal. This idea is emphasised with the use of the second-person pronoun "your", as it involves the reader, who could be of any background, race or culture.
3. The pilot appears to value his personal or family identity over national identity, as his childhood memories of "waiting" for his father may have led him to turn back rather than fulfil his patriotic duty. His inclination towards personal identity over national identity during the flight is ironically what causes him to lose his personal and family identity when he returns home.
4. The narrator feels the education he's received has neglected his identity by not involving stories of people with a similar cultural background to him. "Dem tell me wha dem want to tell me" suggests he feels that the British education system has intentionally hidden his cultural history from him. The way he trivialises British history, e.g. "1066 and all dat", suggests he is angry that he has been purposely closed off from his identity.

Page 42: Individual Experiences

1. Describing the photographer as "finally alone" in his darkroom suggests that he needs separation from society to be able to do his job. Also, the final phrase "they do not care" shows a disconnect between the photographer and the rest of society.
2. Using a first-person narrator throughout presents the speaker's personal experiences and emotions. Phrases such as "my city comes to me" allow the reader to share in this. The use of caesura and ellipsis in the first line suggests the speaker is lost in her thoughts, suggesting she is recounting a very personal experience.
3. The single hare emphasises the soldier's isolation. Its frantic movements "in a threshing circle" remind the soldier of the danger he is in and spurs him on. Similarly, the startled, stunned nature of the hare could reflect the soldier's bewilderment. The hare's "mouth wide / Open silent" reflects the moment when the soldier seems so frightened that he stops and can't move or think.
4. In 'London', the narrator is free to "wander" the streets and describe the suffering that he sees. This contrasts him with the "chartered" city, creating a sense of detachment between the two. This detachment enables the narrator to comment on both the suffering and the institutions who are turning a blind eye to it.

Exam Practice:
Your answer should have an introduction, several paragraphs developing different ideas and a conclusion. You may have covered some of the following points:
- In both 'The Prelude' and 'Remains', the speakers feel isolated after a life-changing experience. The speaker in 'The Prelude' is left feeling isolated after his encounter with the mountain, which leaves him in "solitude". His isolation is emphasised by the contrast with the close relationship he had with nature personified at the start of the extract, where "(led by her)" creates an image of intimacy between the speaker and nature. Similarly, in 'Remains', the soldier is left isolated after killing the looter, as shown by the transition in voice from "we" to "I" — he separates himself from the rest of his patrol. The poem's concluding image of blood on the soldier's hands further shows how he feels completely responsible for the death and has isolated himself.
- There is a change in language after the turning point in each poem, which reflects the speakers' negative experiences. 'The Prelude' changes from beautiful, lyrical language such as "Small circles glittering idly in the moon" to serious language such as "unknown modes of being". This reflects how the speaker now feels unsettled in relating to nature. In 'Remains', the colloquial language of the first four stanzas becomes more figurative after the turning point. Images such as the metaphor of the memory "dug in" suggest that the killing has become complex for the speaker — he cannot process his guilt in simple terms.

- Each character's sleep is troubled as part of their negative experience. In 'Remains', the monosyllabic words "Sleep" and "Dream" on consecutive lines are reminiscent of gunshots, which startle and interrupt the soldier's sleep. Even sleep cannot offer him solace. Similarly, in 'The Prelude', the speaker's recollections of the event "trouble" his "dreams". Placing this unsettling image in the closing line of the extract could show how the memory continues to unsettle him. Showing that both speakers have trouble sleeping allows the reader to empathise with them, as their negative experiences have long-lasting effects.

Page 43: Discussing Context

1. a) From 'The "Storm" may be a reference to...' to '... unionists.'
   b) From 'The reference to...' to '...while she sleepwalks.'
   c) From 'the poem's setting...' to '...have been poisoned.'
2. As a 'Romantic' poet, Wordsworth viewed nature as a powerful force that could inspire or isolate individuals. Owen offers no sense of nature as an inspiring force but instead presents it as utterly destructive.

Section Three — Poetic Techniques

Page 44: Forms of Poetry

1. Each stanza is a similar length with similar line lengths, making the poem look controlled and the narrator seem calm and composed.
2. The rigid form means that every stanza in the poem looks similar. This reflects how "nothing happens" or changes for the soldiers.
3. The poem has an irregular, uneven form with of a mix of line lengths. This reflects the soldier's instability after the shooting, as if he tries to hold it all together but struggles.
4. Shelley subverts the sonnet form in 'Ozymandias' by not using a traditional sonnet rhyme scheme. He had a strong dislike for absolute power, so this disruption of form could be seen as a rebellion against human constructs of power.
5. Both poems have irregular forms that reflect the turbulent reality of conflict. The different stanza lengths and irregular rhyme scheme in 'The Charge of the Light Brigade' emphasise the chaos of conflict, and the uneven line lengths, enjambment and caesurae in 'Bayonet Charge' reflect the confusing reality of battle. Both poems use irregular forms to reflect how conflict consists of sprawling, unpredictable experiences.

Page 45: Poetic Devices

1. The second "safe" is emphasised by the preceding caesura and so appears less naturally in the speech, almost as if the idea of safety became more certain in the pilot's mind.
2. 'London'. Effect: This repeated appeal to hearing emphasises the constant, inescapable cries of misery and adds to the bleak tone of the poem.
   'Remains'. Effect: The repeated "I see" focuses the reader's attention on the graphic visual image, and the onomatopoeic "rips" mimics the sound of bullets tearing into the looter's flesh.
3. The end-stopping emphasises the certainty of the narrator's sense of security, reflecting the strength of the "rock" and "slate".
4. Wordsworth creates a huge contrast between the man who rows "Proud of his skill" and the man who later rows "With trembling oars". The complete destruction of the narrator's confidence by the mountain makes the speaker's fear seem more dramatic.
5. Example: "Bandage up me eye with me own history"
   Effect: The word "bandage" connotes healing and restoration, but here it has caused blindness and represents emotional pain.

Exam Practice:
Your answer should have an introduction, several paragraphs developing different ideas and a conclusion. You may have covered some of the following points:
- 'The Charge of the Light Brigade' and 'Poppies' present loss on contrasting scales. The soldiers in 'The Charge of the Light Brigade' are repeatedly referred to as "the six hundred". This presents them as a single entity which creates a lack of individuality. When the loss is described — as "Not the six hundred" riding back — it is difficult for the reader to connect with it on a personal level. On the other hand, 'Poppies' presents loss through a mother losing her son to the army, or possibly death. Domestic imagery such as the mother saying she "smoothed down" her son's "upturned collar" seems gentle.

Answers

The long vowel sound in "smoothed" implies that she does this slowly, as though she lingers on the memory for as long as possible to remember her son. This portrays her loss in a more personal way than the collective loss of "the six hundred".

• Loss is portrayed as inevitable in both poems. The regular rhythm and repetition in 'The Charge of the Light Brigade', such as "Half a league, half a league, / Half a league onward", mimics the momentum of the soldiers' charge, suggesting that their death is unstoppable. Tennyson's readers would have known when reading the poem that many died in the battle, so this momentum would have been poignant. There is a different inevitability in 'Poppies'. At the end of the poem, the narrator listens to the wind hoping to hear her son's "playground voice". By associating her son leaving to join the army with the memory of him at school, the mother shows that this is not the first time she has lost her son. This suggests that as a parent, the 'loss' of your child is inevitable and comes in lots of different forms.

• Both poems portray loss as something to be remembered. The final stanza of Tennyson's poem commands the reader to "Honour the Light Brigade" and asks "When can their glory fade?" This use of rhetoric shows that the narrator believes the Light Brigade should be remembered by their nation. The reference to "Armistice Sunday" in 'Poppies' — a day to remember the loss and sacrifice of soldiers — shows a similar national mourning. However, the poem shifts to a more personal mourning through the images of poppies placed on "individual war graves" and the mother pinning a poppy onto her son's lapel. Using 'Poppies' as the poem's title highlights the significance of this symbol of remembrance, and there is a sense that both poems are intended as memorials to the lost soldiers.

Page 46: Use of Sound

1. a) The use of sibilance and plosives creates a spitting sound, hinting at anger that the photos will be sidelined in the "supplement".

   b) The use of alliteration draws out each sound and reflects the long stretches of deserted land that the traveller describes.

2. Dharker uses alliteration, such as in the line "pages smoothed and stroked and turned transparent", to create a sense of flow that gives the poem a thoughtful tone.

3. The onomatopoeic "struck" mirrors the sound of the narrator's oars hitting the water, with the repetition of the sound hinting at his panic and desperation.

4. Quote: "that blue crackling air"
   Explanation: The onomatopoeia in "crackling" emphasises the persistent, unsettling sound of gunfire surrounding the soldier.

5. The use of sound in 'Exposure' is arguably more effective as Owen uses it to comment on the men's experiences rather than just illustrating real sounds. Both poems use sibilance to mimic the sound of whizzing bullets or the sea, but the repeated long 'o' sounds in 'Exposure' draw the poem out, reflecting the exhaustion and monotony the soldiers feel.

Page 47: Imagery

1. a) Personification: "Back from the mouth of Hell"
   Effect: Personifying "Hell" by giving it a "mouth" makes it seem more dangerous, making the soldiers' return from it seem all the more miraculous.

   b) Metaphor: "spools of suffering"
   Effect: The metaphor suggests that the cylinders of photographic film have permanently captured the suffering of war.

2. This mixture, e.g. "Sellotape® bandaged", shows how conflict affects even the everyday aspects of life for those left at home.

3. The image of an architect building up a human "layer over layer" reflects how our identities consist of many parts, including layers from our ancestors and society. However, each layer is fragile like a sheet of paper, emphasising that human structures are "never meant to last".

4. The use of casual imagery in the first half of the poem, such as the body being "carted off in the back of a lorry", shows how the narrator had become desensitised to death. However, this death is different — the narrator questions the morality of his actions and the images of the looter start to regain their horror.

Exam Practice:
   Your answer should have an introduction, several paragraphs developing different ideas and a conclusion. You may have covered some of the following points:

• In both 'Tissue' and 'The Prelude', natural imagery is used to present the idea that nature is more powerful than humans. In 'Tissue', the image of the sun as it "shines through" the "borderlines" of maps suggests this as light is physically able to break through human constructs. Similarly, nature is dominant and powerful in 'The Prelude', where the image of the personified mountain striding after the narrator with "measured motion" gives it a calm but intimidating superiority that terrifies the narrator. While this image shows nature's power by focusing on an individual interaction with nature, 'Tissue' presents it by exploring nature's ability to transform entire human constructs.

• While in 'Tissue' nature is presented as an illuminating force, in 'The Prelude' it obscures the narrator's thoughts. The narrator in 'Tissue' uses an imagined image of the wind causing a paper building to "shift", suggesting that if all buildings were paper, nature would be able to enlighten us and reveal their temporary state. In contrast, the image of nature's "huge and mighty forms" in 'The Prelude' suggests that the narrator is unable to understand or process his experience with the mountain. The way the mountain appears here as multiple indistinguishable "forms" suggests that nature unsettles rather than enlightens him.

• Nature is presented as liberating in 'Tissue', but controlling in 'The Prelude'. The image of letting "daylight break / through capitals and monoliths" can be interpreted as nature freeing us from our human constraints. This 'breaking' seems positive rather than destructive, and invites the reader to question the worth of human constructs. In contrast, the narrator's experience in 'The Prelude' changes his initial feeling of freedom in nature to one of oppression. The personification of the "black and huge" mountain peak which "Upreared its head" presents nature as threatening. This instils fear in the narrator and influences him to turn back, implying that nature has the ability to control our thoughts and actions — therefore presenting it as a constraining force.

Page 48: Rhyme and Rhythm

1. Example: "us" (line 36) and "ice" (line 39)
   Effect: The half-rhymes create an unsatisfying, disjointed effect that mirrors the uncomfortable situation the soldiers are in. They could also reflect the idea that the soldiers' lives are unfinished — they've only lived half a life.

2. The poem is written in iambic pentameter. This gives it a natural rhythm that is similar to speech and reinforces the idea that the Duke is talking fluently and confidently to the visitor.

3. The chant-like rhythms create a fast-paced, almost forceful tone that emphasise the narrator's combined feelings of anger and excitement at breaking free from the British structures he finds restrictive. They also connect the poem with the oral tradition — a way of communicating and sharing history, just as the narrator does in these stanzas.

4. The lack of rhyme in both poems creates the impression of natural speech. This emphasises the anecdotal tone of 'Remains' and reflects the soldier struggling to order his thoughts. In 'Poppies', it reflects the domestic tone and suggests that the mother's loss of closeness with her son makes her feel incomplete.

Page 49: Voice

1. The first-person voice makes the presentation of London appear more realistic and personal because it suggests that it comes from the narrator's direct experience.

2. The daughter's voice makes the poem more personal and emotive, and not using the pilot's voice further distances him from society.

3. They suggest that although the narrator is the main voice in the poem, she has relied upon a second figure to fill in the gaps in her knowledge regarding the old city and her past.

4. The Duke's voice is dominant in the poem, making questions, e.g. "Will't please you sit and look at her?", seem more of a command than an invitation. This voice is maintained even when hinting at the dark acts he's committed, making the tone even more sinister.

5. The anonymous third-person voice in 'War Photographer' increases the distance between the reader and the war zone, and allows for a view of war to be presented away from the intensity of conflict. In contrast, 'Exposure', features a collective voice of soldiers. The first-person plural pronouns "us" and "we" show that their painful experience is a shared one, implying that this voice could represent all soldiers facing these conditions.

Answers

Exam Practice:

Your answer should have an introduction, several paragraphs developing different ideas and a conclusion. You may have covered some of the following points:

• 'Checking Out Me History' and 'Kamikaze' use voice to explore the divisions created by conflict. 'Checking Out Me History' uses different voices for the British and Caribbean stanzas. The voice in British stanzas uses a more conventional sentence structure, such as in "Blind me to me own identity", which contrasts with the broken sentences of the chant-like voice of Caribbean stanzas, as in "Toussaint / a slave / with vision". The oral and visual conflict between them may reflect a history of conflict and oppression between the cultures. Similarly, in 'Kamikaze', the voices of the third-person narrator and the pilot's daughter create a split in voice, reflecting how the family has been divided. The pilot's lack of voice underlines this division, as he has become shunned from the poem just like with his family.

• Both poems use voice to show internal conflict. The divided voice in 'Checking Out Me History' conveys the narrator's internal conflict — it is as if both the British and Caribbean voices are a part of him and he does not yet have a unified voice. The concluding claim of "I carving out me identity" suggests he is actively trying to resolve this internal conflict. In 'Kamikaze', the factual, reserved tone of the daughter's direct speech in phrases such as *we too learned / to be silent* hints at her pain and an internal conflict about whether she treated her father unfairly. This is emphasised by the narrative voice that reports her speculations about what her father might have thought, creating a sense of internal uncertainty.

• Both poems feature representations of voices that are not heard in the poem but that contribute to conflict in it. The voices of "dem" in 'Checking Out Me History' are presented as being in direct conflict with the speaker. Even though their identities are never explicitly revealed and the reader doesn't hear the voices directly, "dem" have clearly stoked the speaker's anger. Similarly, the "powerful incantations" in 'Kamikaze' are an example of external voice, as they represent the voices the pilot heard that incited violence and convinced him to undergo the suicide mission. However, both the speaker in 'Checking Out Me History' and the pilot in 'Kamikaze' ultimately seem to rebel against these external voices and make their own decisions.

Page 50: Beginnings of Poems

1. 'Ozymandias'. Effect: The words "traveller" and "antique" give the start of the narrator's anecdote a sense of mystery and create an interesting hook for the reader.
   'My Last Duchess'. Effect: The way the Duke talks about the painting seems cold and possessive, inviting the reader to question what happened to his "last" Duchess.
2. The word "finally" suggests that he is relieved to be alone, as though he's been looking forward to it for some time. There is an implied sense of familiarity and comfort — it is "his" darkroom.
3. The first stanza has a heroic tone with patriotic references, including to a "samurai sword". However, the tone becomes contemplative as the daughter considers her father's decision, then factual as the sombre reality of his rejection is explored.
4. The opening of 'The Charge of the Light Brigade' has an epic quality. Language such as "Charge for the guns!" makes the "six hundred" sound heroic. This contrasts with 'Remains', where a small group of soldiers deal with an everyday mission. The use of colloquial language, such as "one of them legs it", also gives the poem a casual tone.

Page 51: Endings of Poems

1. 'Tissue'. Effect: The use of "your" involves the reader, perhaps encouraging them to think about their own heritage and identity.
   'Ozymandias'. Effect: By highlighting the vastness of the desert, Shelley further emphasises the insignificance of the statue and Ozymandias's rule.
   'Storm on the Island'. Effect: This admission of fear contrasts with the earlier confidence. Describing the storm as a "huge nothing" reflects the narrator's feeling of uneasiness.
2. It suggests that the soldier's fear has transformed him into a dangerous, unpredictable and explosive weapon.
3. The phrase emphasises the bleak and hopeless mood of the poem. The word "plagues" implies that the situation is

widespread and uncontrollable, and by linking marriage with death Blake suggests that all hope has been destroyed.
4. The narrator's mind is haunted by "huge and mighty forms", contrasting with the familiar and rural imagery of the first five lines. This change from an idyllic tone to an ominous one reflects the narrator's change from confidence to uneasiness.

Page 52: Mood

1. 'War Photographer'. Mood: This creates a solemn mood — it's as though developing the photos is a ritual similar to a funeral Mass.
   'The Emigrée'. Mood: This creates a hopeful mood because although the word "shadow" can represent darkness, it is a sign that there is still light to be found in the city.
2. The poem's rhythm mimics the galloping of horses, creating a sense of frantic relentlessness as though death is inevitable. This establishes a frenetic but also tragic mood.
3. There's a mood of liberation in the final stanza as the narrator declares that he is "carving out" his own identity, which appears in stark contrast to the oppressive mood of the first stanza.
4. The domestic imagery in 'Poppies' creates an intimate mood, as though the reader is witnessing a very personal experience of a mother and her loss. In contrast, the images of family life in 'Kamikaze' create a nostalgic mood which may have made the pilot turn back, but ironically the mood when he returns is cold.

Exam Practice:

Your answer should have an introduction, several paragraphs developing different ideas and a conclusion. You may have covered some of the following points:

• The beginnings of both 'Remains' and 'War Photographer' feature a disconnect between the mood of the poem and the subject matter. In 'Remains', the opening of "On another occasion" creates a relaxed mood which contrasts with the description of the soldiers shooting the looter. This juxtaposition creates a sense of unease, perhaps reflecting the soldier's struggle to adapt to life back home whilst still being a soldier. In 'War Photographer', the simile comparing the darkroom to a "church" and the photographer to a "priest" creates a calm mood that contrasts with the "spools of suffering" on the reels. These conflicts between mood and content can be interpreted as reflecting the discomfort caused by war.

• Both poems feature a turning point that corresponds with a change of mood. The turning point in line 17 of 'Remains' sees a change from the initially casual mood to a more serious, introspective and haunting mood as the narrator's guilt takes hold. Similarly, in 'War Photographer', the mood becomes angrier after the turning point in line 13, with the mood intensified by the developing photographs showing victims of war. Both changes in mood emphasise how the narrators are affected by the reality of conflict — the soldier in 'Remains' cannot "flush" the looter's death from his mind, and the photographer in 'War Photographer' doesn't understand society's apathy towards suffering.

• In addition to the overall changes in mood, each poem features abrupt but temporary changes. The single words "Sleep" and "Dream" in lines 22 and 23 of 'Remains' are each followed by a caesura, separating them from the rest of the line. This gives an impression of gunshots being fired and creates a sudden break in the conversational mood of the poem. Similarly, in 'War Photographer', the plosive 'b' and 'p' sounds in the phrase "Belfast. Beirut. Phnom Penh." mimic the sound of gunfire, creating a sudden shift from the solemn mood of the rest of the first stanza. In each poem, it is as though the chaos of conflict has unexpectedly broken through the earlier mood, bringing a sudden and jarring change.

Page 53: Analysing Language, Structure and Form

1. a) Using phonetic spellings such as "dem" or "me" to represent his Caribbean roots gives the speaker a sense of identity, which has not been granted to him by the British system.
   b) The speaker switches focus between British history and Caribbean history. He talks at length about his own cultural history but quickly skips over British history and culture, showing he doesn't value them as much.
   c) There is no regular rhyme scheme, but simple rhymes such as "dat" and "cat" are used in the British stanzas to make them sound childish, whereas complex rhymes in the Caribbean stanza reflect its rich cultural history.

Answers

Answers

Section Four — Exam Buster

Pages 54-55: Planning Your Answer

1. a) <u>Compare</u> the <u>presentation</u> of <u>conflict</u> in 'Bayonet Charge' and one other poem from 'Power and Conflict'.
   b) <u>Compare</u> how the theme of <u>memory</u> is <u>presented</u> in 'Kamikaze' and one other poem from 'Power and Conflict'.
   c) <u>Compare</u> how ideas about <u>identity</u> are <u>explored</u> in 'Checking Out Me History' and one other poem from 'Power and Conflict'.

2. a) Poem: 'Storm on the Island'
   Explanation: Both poems present nature as a powerful force that is able to shape each speaker's emotions and experiences.
   b) Poem: 'War Photographer'
   Explanation: Both poems present individuals who are affected and shaped by their memories and experiences of conflict.
   c) Poem: 'Ozymandias'
   Explanation: The Duke and Ozymandias are two powerful individuals who both exhibit arrogance.

3. Point One: 'Bayonet Charge' and 'The Charge of the Light Brigade' use imagery to emphasise the horror of conflict.
   Point Two: The forms of the poems reflect the chaos of conflict.
   Point Three: Sound is used to reflect the physical impact of conflict.

4. Evidence for Point One.
   'Bayonet Charge': "He lugged a rifle numb as a smashed arm"
   'The Charge of the Light Brigade': "Into the jaws of Death, / Into the mouth of Hell"
   Evidence for Point Two.
   'Bayonet Charge': Irregular rhythm, uneven line lengths
   'The Charge of the Light Brigade': Driving rhythm
   Evidence for Point Three.
   'Bayonet Charge': 'h' sounds in "hot khaki, his sweat heavy"
   'The Charge of the Light Brigade': Sibilance in "sabre stroke / Shatter'd and sunder'd."

Page 56: Comparing Poems

1. a) whereas   b) In contrast   c) similarly
2. Both 'Remains' and 'War Photographer' show how guilt can affect individuals. In 'Remains', the figurative language in "he's here in my head" shows how the soldier's guilt over killing the looter mentally disturbs him, as if he can't escape it. Similarly, the photographer in 'War Photographer' is disturbed by his feeling of guilt. The reference to "ordinary pain which simple weather can dispel" hints that he feels guilty about how comfortable life is in England. For both characters, this sense of guilt only seems to affect them after they have returned home.

Page 57: Structuring Your Answer

1. Point: Both 'Exposure' and 'Storm on the Island' present nature as a dangerous force.
   Example: the winds "knive" the soldiers
   Explain: personification giving the impression that nature is attacking the men.
   Example: the islanders are "bombarded" by the storm
   Explain: creating the image of a bomber plane besieging the island.
   Develop: Comparing the weather to weapons heightens the threat that nature poses to the characters in each poem.

2. a) The islanders in 'Storm on the Island' feel "prepared" for the storm.
   b) In 'The Emigrée', the speaker's city "lies down in front of" her.

3. Point: 'Bayonet Charge' and 'The Charge of the Light Brigade' use imagery to emphasise the horror of conflict.
   Example 1: "He lugged a rifle numb as a smashed arm"
   Explain 1: Simile predicts the soldier being injured.
   Example 2: "Into the jaws of Death, / Into the mouth of Hell"
   Explain 2: Personification presents charge as more dangerous.
   Develop: Poets' use of vivid imagery reminds the reader of the very real threat of death in a conflict setting.

Page 58: Introductions and Conclusions

1. c and e should be ticked.
2. b is the better conclusion as it summarises the main points as well as mentioning appropriate context, whereas a doesn't summarise the main points and introduces new points.

Pages 59-62: Marking Sample Answers

1. Grade band: 4-5 — Explanation: The answer compares the poems clearly. It shows an understanding of ideas, form and the effect on the reader. However, it needs more analysis of language.
2. a) Grade band: 8-9 — Explanation: This answer gives an insightful comparison of the poems with precise examples from each. It offers detailed analysis of language and structure.
   b) Grade band: 6-7 — Explanation: This answer offers a thoughtful comparison of the poems with analysis of language and form. Some more detailed analysis of language would increase the level.
3. Grade band: 8-9 — Explanation: This answer is a strong and detailed comparison, with plenty of appropriate examples from each poem. Language, structure and form have been closely analysed. It gives a detailed exploration of how techniques make the reader feel, as well as referencing contextual information.

Page 63: Writing Well

1. 'The Charge of the Light Brigade' and 'Bayonet Charge' both **emphasise** the sounds of battle. **Tennyson** repeats the **onomatopoeic** verb "thunder'd" to mimic the noise of the cannons that the soldiers faced**.** Similarly, in '**B**ayonet **C**harge', the metaphor "blue crackling air" vividly **depicts** the noise of machine gun fire by using forceful **conson**a**nts** such as 'b' and 'k'.
2. When the storm arrives in 'Storm on the Island', enjambment is used rather than end-stopping as this gives the reader the sense that the islanders' original feeling of safety has disappeared.
3. The narrator of 'War Photographer' describes the photographer as he develops his photos. The film reels are described as "spools of suffering set out in ordered rows", which not only evokes the image of soldiers' graves laid out row upon row, but also suggests that the photographer is able to restructure the chaos of war into something more ordered.

Page 64: Exam-Style Questions

Each answer should have an introduction, several paragraphs developing different ideas and a conclusion. You may have covered some of the following points:

1. • The speaker in 'Storm on the Island' describes the island as physically barren, whilst the city in 'London' is barren of morality. In 'Storm on the Island', the description of the "wizened earth" and the frequent use of negatives such as "no" and "Nor" create a cumulative sense of barrenness. The island's emptiness is ironically a positive thing for the speaker, as in the context of the storm it means nothing can be lost. In a different way, the speaker in 'London' shows the city is morally barren. The symbolic colour of black in the image of the "black'ning church" implies that rather than being a symbol of morality and purity, the church has come to represent corruption and immorality. The black may also allude to the soot and pollution of the Industrial Revolution, which Blake loathed because of how it dirtied London and immorally exploited the city's children.
   • The speaker in 'Storm on the Island' shows a sense of pride towards the island, whereas the narrator in 'London' feels anger towards the city. In 'Storm on the Island', the speaker describes how houses are built "squat" and with "good slate" — they are proud of their strength and feel prepared for the storm. This pride is emphasised in the colloquial tone in "you know what I mean", which suggests the speaker is happy to engage with the reader and share his experience of the island with them. By contrast, in 'London', the narrator's anger is shown through the repetition of "In every" in the second stanza. There is the impression that he says the phrase with increasing force, becoming angrier in listing more social problems. The repetition and use of simple language in the first three lines of the stanza build to the controversial image of the "mind-forged manacles", giving more emphasis to his claim that the citizens are failing to help themselves.
   • 'Storm on the Island' presents the speaker as feeling secure as part of a community, whereas the narrator in 'London' appears isolated in the city. Despite the islanders' geographic isolation, they seem to be a close community. This is shown through the third-person plural pronoun "we", which suggests they endure everything together, including their fear of the storm. A reader might therefore be puzzled by the islanders' seeming desire for "company", but this may reveal their underlying insecurities caused by the storm. In contrast, the first-person narration used

Answers

throughout 'London' encapsulates the narrator's isolation. The repeated "I hear" makes it seem as though no one else hears or sees the social issues he does. In addition, the speaker's rhetoric in the powerful repetition implies that he wants the reader to join him in his criticism of this society.

2. • The Duke in 'My Last Duchess' has negative memories of his past marriage, whereas the speaker in 'Checking Out Me History' speaks fondly of his cultural history. The Duke's description of the Duchess as "she liked whate'er / She looked on" is euphemistic as it seems to present her as friendly, but the context of the her apparent death suggests that he is in fact angry at her perceived flirtatiousness. The fact that he slanders the Duchess even after her death might invoke shock or sadness in the reader. In contrast, the speaker in 'Checking Out Me History' presents "Nanny de maroon" as a "see-far woman / of mountain dream". The lyrical language reflects his admiration for figures from his cultural past. The short, broken lines of the Caribbean stanzas force the reader to slow down and enjoy his cultural history.
• It could be argued that both speakers give a skewed account of past events. The dramatic monologue form of 'My Last Duchess' means the Duke is able to present the past as he pleases. The visitor is told that the Duchess's "looks went everywhere", but he has no chance to reply as the Duke quickly and defensively asserts "Sir, 'twas all one!" and continues his rant with no space for an alternative view. Similarly, the form of 'Checking Out Me History' allows the speaker to give a comically simplistic account of British history. Phrases such as "de man who discover de balloon" suggest the speaker trivialises British history out of frustration at not being taught his "own history". The forms of both poems reflect each speaker's sense of power over the poem.
• The Duke uses the memory of his Duchess to serve as a warning to others, whereas the speaker in 'Checking Out Me History' wishes to move on from his past. "That's my last Duchess painted on the wall" suggests that the Duke has kept possession of his last Duchess, even though their relationship is in the past. Presenting her as an object suggests that he is now using her as a kind of warning to others. On the other hand, the speaker in 'Checking Out Me History' wishes to move away from his past and states that he is "carving out" his identity. The forcefulness of "carving" hints at the strength of the speaker's disdain for his previous identity and suggests his identity is like a sculpture which he will take pride in.

3. • In 'Ozymandias', nature damages human structures, whereas in 'Bayonet Charge', humans damage nature. In 'Ozymandias', the "shatter'd visage" of the statue lies "Half sunk" in the desert. The words "Half" and "shatter'd" connote incompleteness, showing how the statue has been eroded by the desert. The poem's gradually changing rhyme scheme also reflects the gradual decaying of the statue. In contrast, what was once a green field in 'Bayonet Charge' has become a "field of clods" in the war. The word "clods" suggests the field has been reduced to worthless lumps of earth by "Stumbling" soldiers and heavy artillery. This was common in World War One, where large areas of natural landscapes were destroyed by the war.
• Both poems present nature as being able to outlast all aspects of human life. In 'Ozymandias', the desert is "boundless and bare", suggesting that no life can grow or live there. The desert even outlasts "works" that humans have made in their name, such as the decaying statue. In 'Bayonet Charge', the "green hedge" remains — Hughes mentions it twice to emphasise its survival, suggesting that despite human destructiveness, nature will still outlive them. The poems present contrasting ideas of how nature endures — in 'Ozymandias', the desert is "bare" and barren, while the "green hedge" in 'Bayonet Charge' is a symbol of life, emphasised by the colour green which symbolises fertility.
• The poems present a stark contrast between nature and human flaws. The combination of alliteration and sibilance in "lone and level sands stretch" gives a calm serenity to the desert, as the sounds reflect that of a gentle breeze. This serenity is further emphasised when contrasted with Ozymandias's brash words on the statue's pedestal. Similarly, the image in 'Bayonet Charge' of a "yellow hare" with "its mouth wide / Open silent" shows the innocence of nature through a defenceless animal, contrasting with the destruction of the "threshing circle" that it crawls in — having been injured by the fighting. This horrifies the reader, who is left to question the flaws of humanity, which starts wars that are destructive to both humans and nature.

4. • Both 'War Photographer' and 'Poppies' present suffering as an effect of conflict. The image in 'War Photographer' of "running children in a nightmare heat" creates a disturbing image of children running in a kind of hell, as though their suffering goes beyond the normal bounds of reality. The mother's suffering in 'Poppies' is shown when her stomach makes "tucks, darts, pleats". This sewing imagery might reflect how the mother feels sick with grief after losing her son and how she feels unsettled at home. Moreover, the monosyllabic words emphasise her pain — they are short and sharp, with the phrase mimicking a stabbing action. Both poems show that it is not only soldiers who suffer as an effect of war — families and innocent civilians also do.
• The poems present psychological suffering as a consequence of conflict. In 'War Photographer', the photographer has flashbacks as the photos develop — his hands "tremble", showing that the images disturb him, possibly on a deep psychological level. Similarly, in 'Poppies', the mother remembers her words "slowly melting" as she said goodbye to her son. The word "melting" suggests her composure deteriorated as she was overcome by grief and pain. Both individuals' mental suffering is shown through physical effects — the photographer's trembling hands and the mother struggling to talk.
• The photographer is able to partially detach himself from the effects of conflict, whereas the mother in 'Poppies' seems unable to detach herself from them. The photographer appears emotionally detached in war zones — he does "what someone must" and photographs the dead man. The simplicity of this phrase alludes to how he must suppress his emotions to do his job. His detachment is necessary to allow him to document this suffering in the hope that the wider world will do more about the 'stain' of wars on "foreign dust". Conversely, it is as though the mother is overcome by the grief of losing her son to conflict. Although she uses sensory memories as a way to maintain a sense of closeness with her son, the prickly "blackthorns" of his hair imply that she cannot fully detach herself from this feeling of pain, and that conflict infiltrates even these intimate memories.

5. • Both 'The Emigrée' and 'Tissue' highlight the importance of the past in shaping human identity. In 'The Emigrée', the speaker presents her childhood "country" as central to her identity. She refers to it throughout the poem even though she "left it as a child". The use of "branded" to describe the "impression" it left on her suggests that it had a formational impact on her identity. Similarly, in 'Tissue', individual identities are built up through heritage and past experiences. The poem implies that identity is built up with "layer over layer" of human experiences through the generations — the repetition of "layer" reflecting this accumulation. Heritage being recorded on "smoothed and stroked" pages shows its important status in forming identity.
• Both poems seem to reject notions of national identity and are instead more welcoming of a global identity. In 'The Emigrée', the phrase "frontiers rise between us, close like waves" hints negatively at national division and creates the sense that the speaker is being closed in on. Rumens could be hinting at the destructiveness of nationalism and national identity, as this turmoil would have presumably created many refugees. Similarly, in 'Tissue', the phrase "Maps too. The sun shines through / their borderlines" consists of mostly monosyllabic words separated by a caesura, which emphasises how borders, and by extension national identities, are divisive and restrictive. With concepts such as national identity being presented in both poems as divisive, the poets might therefore be implying that people should focus more on global identity and togetherness.
• Both poems explore the theme of childhood identity. The speaker in 'The Emigrée' refuses to abandon her childhood identity and is defiant in wanting "every coloured molecule" of her "child's vocabulary". The imagery shows the vividness of her childhood memories and suggests she's actively trying to reconnect to them. Her refusal to abandon this childhood identity may be why she is accused of "being dark" in her new city. In contrast, childhood identity is valued in 'Tissue'. The recording of "who was born to whom" implies a permanence to identity at the start of life by recording specific details. By presenting the recording of this information, Dharker reinforces the value of childhood identity as central to human life.